𝕸𝖊𝖙𝖍𝖚𝖊𝖓'𝖘 𝕸𝖔𝖓𝖔𝖌𝖗𝖆𝖕𝖍𝖘 𝖔𝖓 𝕻𝖍𝖞𝖘𝖎𝖈𝖆𝖑 𝕾𝖚𝖇𝖏𝖊𝖈𝖙𝖘

General Editor: B. L. WORSNOP, B.Sc., Ph.D.

THE EARTH'S MAGNETISM

THE EARTH'S MAGNETISM

by

S. CHAPMAN

M.A., D.Sc., F.R.S.

PROFESSOR OF MATHEMATICS, IMPERIAL COLLEGE OF
SCIENCE AND TECHNOLOGY, UNIVERSITY OF LONDON

WITH 35 DIAGRAMS

09447

METHUEN & CO. LTD.
36 ESSEX STREET, W.C.
London

First published in 1936

PRINTED IN GREAT BRITAIN

TO

J. A. FLEMING

AND TO

THE MEMORY OF

L. A. BAUER

OF THE

CARNEGIE INSTITUTE OF WASHINGTON

PREFACE

THIS monograph contains a brief but fairly broad account of our present knowledge of the earth's magnetic field and its changes. The mathematical developments of the subject are barely indicated, and the space available has not allowed more than passing reference to such cognate topics as the aurora, earth currents, solar phenomena, or radio research. For the same reason historical details, controversial theoretical discussions, and mention of the authors to whom individual results are due, are almost wholly excluded. I hope, shortly, in collaboration with Professor J. Bartels, to publish a much more extensive and detailed account of the subject.

S. CHAPMAN

CONTENTS

LIST OF PRINCIPAL SYMBOLS

(in order of introduction)

I   magnetic dip (p. 1).

D   ,,   declination (p. 1), (also used for magnetic disturbance, p. 31).

F   ,,   total intensity (p. 1).

H   ,,   horizontal force (p. 1).

Z   ,,   vertical force, positive downwards (p. 1).

V   ,,   ,,   ,,   (always positive) (p. 1).

X   ,,   north force (p. 1).

Y   ,,   east force (p. 1).

Γ gauss (unit of magnetic force) (p. 6).

γ gamma, $10^{-6}\Gamma$ (smaller unit of magnetic force) (p. 6).

M   magnetic moment (p. 7; also see p. 15).

a radius of sphere (p. 15).

J   intensity of magnetization (p. 15).

Ω magnetic potential (p. 15).

H_0, Z_0 ,,   horizontal and vertical force at the equator of a uniformly magnetized sphere (p. 17).

l latitude (p. 21).

λ east longitude (p. 21).

S   solar daily magnetic variation from all days (p. 31).

L   lunar daily magnetic variation from all days (p. 31).

S_q, S_d solar daily variation from quiet or disturbed days (p. 34).

S_D disturbance daily variation ($S-S_q$ or S_d-S_q) (p. 35).

D_m daily mean on disturbed or all days less daily mean for quiet days (p. 35).

D_{st} disturbance variation depending on storm-time (pp. 36, 76).

D_i the irregular part of the disturbance variation (p. 36).

a_n, b_n Fourier coefficients of daily magnetic variations; $n = 1, 2, 3, 4 \ldots$ (p. 50).

S_q^i, S_q^e the internal and external parts of the S_q field (p. 53).

κ electrical conductivity within the earth (p. 53).

μ magnetic permeability within the earth (p. 55).

L^i, L^e the internal and external parts of the L field (p. 71).

CHAPTER I

THE MAIN FIELD AND THE SECULAR VARIATION

The Magnetic Elements

IN the space directly accessible to man and his instruments, at or near the earth's surface, there is a natural magnetic field. This is revealed most simply by its directive effect on a magnetized needle. The ordinary compass needle is weighted so as to swing horizontally; a magnetized needle freely pivotted and perfectly balanced will in general not be horizontal. Such a needle is called a *dip* needle; its "north-seeking" end dips below the horizontal at an angle I called the magnetic *dip* (I is reckoned negative if this end is uppermost, as is the case throughout most of the southern hemisphere). The inclination of the compass needle (that is, of its north-seeking half) to the geographical north is called the magnetic *declination* D (or, by seamen, the magnetic *variation*); it may be either west or east, and is usually reckoned positive if to the east.

The intensity of the magnetic force at any point will be denoted by F. Its horizontal and vertical (downward) components will be denoted by H and Z; H is always reckoned positive, but Z is reckoned negative if upwards. When the vertical component is considered regardless of sign it will be denoted by V (always positive). The northern and eastern components of H will be denoted by X, Y respectively. All the quantities X, Y, Z, H, F, D, I,

are called magnetic *elements :* the following relations hold
between them :

$$F^2 = H^2 + Z^2 = H^2 + V^2 \qquad Z = F \sin I$$
$$H = F \cos I \qquad\qquad Y = H \sin D$$
$$X = H \cos D \qquad\qquad \tan I = Z/H$$
$$H^2 = X^2 + Y^2 \qquad\qquad \tan D = Y/X.$$

Three elements are needed to specify the field at a point.
Those usually chosen are H, I, D ; H, V, D ; or X, Y, Z.

ISOMAGNETIC MAPS

The distribution of the magnetic field over the earth's
surface can be represented by maps on which lines called
isomagnetic lines are drawn. These are such that each
passes through all the points at which a particular magnetic element has a definite (indicated) value. Thus
there is a set of such lines, forming an isomagnetic map,
for each element. Special names have been given to the
isomagnetic lines for certain elements. Those for declination are called *isogonic* lines, for dip *isoclinic* lines,
for the total intensity (F) *isodynamic* lines. The isomagnetic lines for H, V, X, Y are simply called lines of
equal horizontal, vertical, north or east force. Isomagnetic
maps may, of course, be drawn on any projection.

Another valuable magnetic map is that containing the
lines of horizontal magnetic force, drawn so that their
direction at each point is that of the horizontal force at
the point. Fig. 1, of epoch about 1830, shows the map for
the northern hemisphere (it also shows the lines of equal dip).
This map gives a good pictorial representation of the
direction of the horizontal part of the field, which governs
the compass ; but it is not so useful to seamen as the isogonic map (Fig. 2), since the latter more easily enables
the compass direction at any point to be read off by interpolation with fair accuracy. The isogonic lines themselves give, however, no immediate indication of the general
distribution of compass direction, such as Fig. 1 affords.

They have what may be considered an artificial complication near the geographical poles, because in the near neighbourhood of each pole the direction of H is nearly constant, while the north direction changes through four right angles as we go round the pole in a circuit however small.

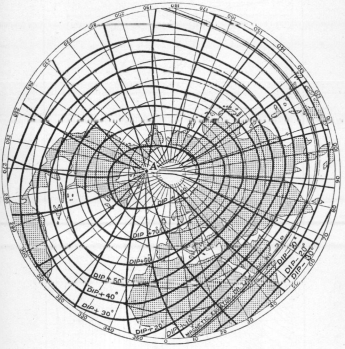

FIG. 1.

Hence all values of the declination occur near the poles, and all the isogonic lines pass through these points.

All the isogonic lines also pass through certain points, called *magnetic poles* (or *dip poles*), where H vanishes and $I = \pm 90°$, because near such a point the north direction

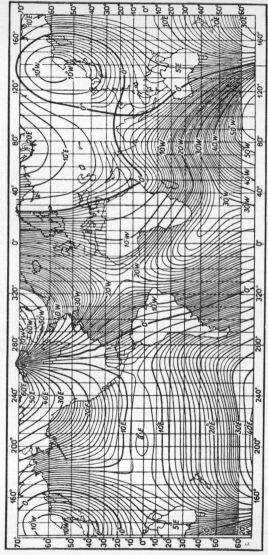

Fig. 2.—Admiralty chart of isogonic lines (or lines of equal declination) for 1922.

is nearly constant, while that of H changes through four right angles as we go round the dip pole in a circuit however small. The lines of horizontal force in Fig. 1 also all converge to such points, but not to the geographical poles.

There are two principal dip poles, whose approximate positions in 1922 were 71° N., 96° W. and 73° S., 156° E. The former is called the north, and the latter the south magnetic pole: at both of them H = 0 (by definition), while Z and I are positive at the north pole, and negative at the south pole. There are also other dip poles of minor importance, in various localities of intense magnetic

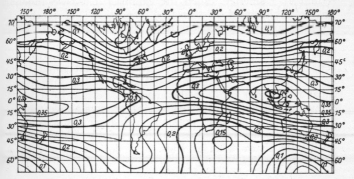

FIG. 3.—Lines of equal horizontal intensity (H), 1922.

irregularity, where magnetic ores situated not far from the surface so greatly distort the general field, over a small area, as to reduce H to zero at one or more points. In general, however, references to the dip poles will in this book relate only to the two principal poles.

The isomagnetic lines for F, H, V and I are (in the main) simple curves approximately parallel to each other and centred round the two dip poles; Fig. 3 shows the isomagnetic lines for the element H, for 1922. Owing to slight departures of the field from a regular distribution, however, the four sets of curves are not quite identical in shape. The curve $V = 0$ is, however, necessarily the same as the curve $I = 0$; this curve, at all points of which a perfectly balanced magnetized needle sets horizontal, is called the magnetic *equator*. To the north of this curve Z and I are positive, that is, the dip needle points downwards, while to the south of it the dip needle points upwards.

Units and Force Values.

The unit of force used for F, H, V, X, Y is the c.g.s. electromagnetic unit, the gauss (indicated by the symbol Γ). A unit 10^{-5} smaller, called the gamma (γ), is also much used in publications on terrestrial magnetism; $1\Gamma = 10^5\gamma$.

The value of the vertical force V varies from zero on the magnetic equator to about $0 \cdot 6\Gamma$ at the magnetic poles; H varies from zero at the poles to about $0 \cdot 3\Gamma$ on the magnetic equator—though it is not quite constant along the line. Thus F ranges from about $0 \cdot 3\Gamma$ at the magnetic equator to about $0 \cdot 6\Gamma$ at the magnetic poles. In a few disturbed localities F falls below $0 \cdot 3\Gamma$ or rises above $0 \cdot 6\Gamma$, to 3Γ or more at some points; such local disturbances distort the isomagnetic lines in their neighbourhood, but small-scale charts such as Figs. 2, 3 do not show these local irregularities.

Absolute Magnetic Measurements and Instruments.

In principle it is a simple matter to measure the *direction* of the magnetic field, that is, to determine D and I. In practice, however, it is not easy to achieve the desired accuracy (to $0 \cdot 1$ minute of arc), especially in the case of I. Usually D is determined by means of a compass needle with the aid of a meridian mark. Until recently I was obtained by use of a dip needle, but an electrical instrument called a *dip inductor* is now often used instead. In this instrument a coil is rotated about an axis whose direction can be varied (and measured); it is moved until a galvanometer registers no induced current in the rotating coil. The axis of rotation is then aligned along the field, so that its inclination is I. Yet a third method of finding I is to measure H and Z separately, and to use the relation

$$\tan I = Z/H.$$

When D and I are known, all the elements can be found if H also is measured, and this is the usual practice, following a method due to Gauss. The instrument used is called a magnetometer. A freely suspended horizontal bar magnet of magnetic moment M and moment of inertia mk^2 oscillates about its centre O in the time T given by $2\pi\sqrt{(mk^2/MH)}$; if an unmagnetized body of simple form, and therefore easily calculable moment of inertia $m'k'^2$, is attached to the needle, T is changed to T', given by

$$2\pi\sqrt{\{(mk^2 + m'k'^2)/MH\}}.$$

By measuring T and T', and using the known value of $m'k'^2$, the values of mk^2 and MH are found. A further experiment is then made by which M/H is found, so that, knowing MH and M/H, H itself is determined. This experiment is called the deflection experiment, because the original bar magnet is used to modify the earth's field near a compass needle (centre C), which is thereby deflected through an angle θ. The bar magnet is placed horizontally, pointing toward C, so as to be perpendicular either to the original or the deflected direction of the compass needle; in the first case $\tan \theta = 2M/Hr^3$, in the second case $\sin \theta = 2M/Hr^3$, where r is the distance OC. In either case, knowing r and θ, M/H is found. This Gaussian method of finding H is still widely used, but it does not readily yield the desired accuracy (to 1γ).

As in the case of I, electrical methods of measuring H (and also V) are coming into use, because of their greater ease, speed and accuracy. In the Schuster-Smith coil magnetometer, the horizontal component of the earth's field is annulled at the centre of a coil of wire of known dimensions, by adjusting the current flowing in the coil: the measurement of the current determines H if the

constants of the coil are known.   Dye constructed a somewhat similar instrument which measures V.   La Cour has
devised another type of vertical force magnetometer, in
which the quantity measured is the current-flow induced
when a horizontal coil is suddenly given a half turn about
a horizontal axis, so as to reverse the magnetic flux through
it.   Coil-magnetometers are difficult to calibrate absolutely,
but when this has been done they can readily be used to
standardize other magnetometers of the same type.

MAGNETIC OBSERVATORIES, VARIOMETERS AND MAGNETOGRAPHS

The earth's magnetic field is constantly changing, and
its variations are recorded continuously by photography
at a considerable number of institutions called magnetic
observatories, widely distributed over the earth.   The
oldest magnetic observatories date back to about 1840,
and in the early years, before photographic methods had
been introduced, hourly eye observations of the magnetic
elements were made.   The elements recorded are usually
H, V and D.   The instruments used are called *variometers*,
because they are not designed to give the absolute values
of the elements, but only to show their small variations.
The time scale of the records obtained, which are called
magnetographs, is usually about 15 mm. per hour, though
some observatories also have quick-recording variometers
with a time scale twelve to twenty times as open.   The
scale of force on magnetographs usually lies within the
range 3 to 10γ per mm. (for H and V) or (for D) about
1′ per mm., though practice varies.

At a magnetic observatory there are both absolute
instruments and variometers : the former are used to
calibrate the " *base-lines* " from which the readings of the
magnetograph curves are measured.

MAGNETIC SURVEYS

The distribution of magnetic force over the earth is
not given in sufficient detail by measures made at the

magnetic observatories alone. Series of observations made at a closer network of points, on sea as well as on land, are needed for this purpose. These operations are called magnetic *surveys*. Portable absolute instruments are used, those for land and sea surveys being somewhat different in design.

Land magnetic surveys are usually made nationally, and sea surveys by vessels of the leading maritime nations. But such national efforts left much of the globe surveyed very imperfectly if at all. To supply the need for a comprehensive world survey, filling up the large gaps in magnetic data, by land and (still more) by ocean expeditions, the Carnegie Institution of Washington, through the initiative of the late L. A. Bauer, founded a Department of Terrestrial Magnetism (1904). This has taken " the world as its parish," with immense benefit to the science ; it has made extensive magnetic surveys on land and sea, using for its ocean surveys a specially constructed non-magnetic ship (unhappily lost by fire, with its commander Ault, at Apia, Samoa, in 1929) ; it has instituted and maintains two magnetic observatories in Australia and Peru ; and in numerous other ways it has made or assisted important magnetic investigations in many parts of the world. The British Admiralty is constructing a new non-magnetic ship for ocean magnetic surveying.

Since the earth's field is always changing, magnetic surveys have to be renewed at intervals, to keep our knowledge of the earth's field up to date. Owing to the irregularity of the changes, which cannot be predicted far ahead with any certainty, a gap in our knowledge for any region, due to a long absence of observations there, is irremediable. The interval between surveys should be from 15 to 30 years, depending on the rapidity of variation over each area, as judged by the records of the nearest observatories.

Extensive magnetic surveys usually need the co-operation of one or more magnetic observatories in their vicinity. This is because they generally extend over months, and sometimes over years, and it is necessary to reduce the observations, taken in different months and at different times of day, to a common epoch. Each observation is therefore corrected by the difference, derived by interpolation from data for the nearest magnetic observatories, between the value of the element at the time of observation, and its mean value for a period (generally a year) centred at the chosen epoch; this is usually near the middle of the period covered by the survey.

THE SECULAR MAGNETIC VARIATION

The successive annual mean values of the magnetic elements at an observatory, or the values obtained for different epochs by magnetic surveys, show that the earth's field undergoes *secular* changes, that is, changes long continued in the same sense, though not necessarily or usually at a constant rate. This is called the secular magnetic variation; over a long period the total change is very considerable, though it may not continue indefinitely without reversal.

The existence of the secular variation of declination was discovered in 1634 by Gellibrand at London, the declination itself having been known at least since the fifteenth century. In 1576 Norman discovered the magnetic dip; the secular variation of dip came to light during the seventeenth century. Knowledge of the secular variation in F or H is more recent, for absolute measurements of intensity date only from about 1826, though relative measures were made earlier, in the latter part of the eighteenth century, by measuring MH at different places and times with the same magnet (of unknown and possibly inconstant M). Thus our knowledge of the secular variation goes back much farther for the direction of the earth's field than for its intensity.

Fig. 4 illustrates the change in direction of the magnetic force at London since about 1580. It shows the curve that would have been traced on a sphere, during this period, by the end of a dip needle freely pivotted at the centre of the sphere. The curve is an oval, apparently about three-quarters complete, suggesting a cyclic variation in about 480 years. But the variations at other stations suggest rather different periods. There is no certainty that the secular variation is really periodic at any station, and little likelihood that for the earth as a whole it has any dominant true period. It has been stated by certain writers that the earth's magnetic poles are revolving round the geographical poles, but the evidence is against rather than for this conclusion.

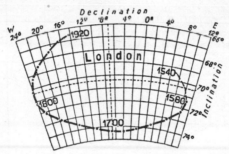

FIG. 4.—The direction of the magnetic force at London, since 1580.

The distribution of annual change in each element at any epoch can be represented on maps by lines of equal annual change : these lines are called *isopors*, and the maps are called *isoporic* maps. Fig. 5 shows such a map for the total intensity. It shows regions of specially rapid decrease in the southern oceans below latitude 30° S. ; the area of increasing intensity is much smaller than that of decreasing intensity, and the maximum rates of increase are in general less than those of decrease. Thus on the whole the earth's field is at present decreasing in intensity. This average decrease appears to have been progressive for about a century, though the regions of most rapid change may not have been always the same.

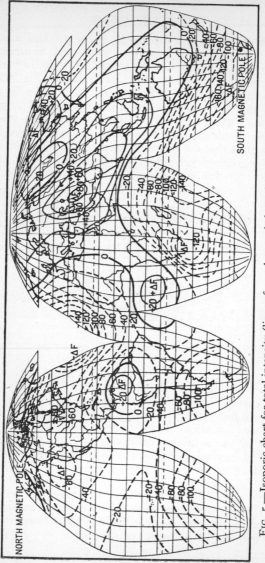

Fig. 5.—Isoporic chart for total intensity (lines of equal annual change) approximate epoch, 1920–1925. (Position of isopors in high latitudes, especially near the magnetic poles, very uncertain.)

The earth's field as a whole is of a simple character, but the distribution of the secular variation is decidedly less simple. Bartels has expressed the difference between the two by saying that the earth's field is a planetary phenomenon, while the secular variation is a regional one.

Mercanton has sought to throw light on the secular variation over much longer periods of time—geological ages—by measuring the magnetization of certain lava beds that appear to have remained undistorted since they were first deposited. It is supposed that just before lava solidifies it acquires induced magnetization, in a direction corresponding with the local direction of the earth's field, and thereafter preserves it without change. Thus it should indicate the dip of the field at that place and epoch, and also the declination, if there has been no general drift or rotation of the land on which it lies. The measurements suggest remarkable changes in the direction of the field: these may be attributed either to a real change in the field, or to a large motion of the underlying land strata over the body of the earth. The enquiry is interesting and important, but no certain conclusion can yet be drawn from it.

The Earth a Great Magnet

William Gilbert of Colchester, Queen Elizabeth's physician, seems to have been the first man to attain to a true conception of the general character of the earth's magnetic field. This, and the experiments that guided him, are described in his treatise " De Magnete," published in A.D. 1600. He cut a spherical piece of the naturally magnetized mineral called lodestone, and examined the distribution of direction of the magnetic force over its surface by means of tiny magnetized needles freely pivotted. He saw that the distribution of dip agreed with what was known of the earth's field. Hence he concluded that the earth is itself a great magnet, similar to his magnetized sphere except in size : and also that its magnetic influence proceeds from within, whereas his contemporaries thought that compass needles were directed by the pole star.

Three centuries later Faraday introduced his conception of lines and tubes of force. Their direction can be shown experimentally by means of iron filings. Fig. 6 shows the lines of force for a uniformly magnetized sphere; hence it indicates how the earth's field is likely to vary in direction at points above the earth.

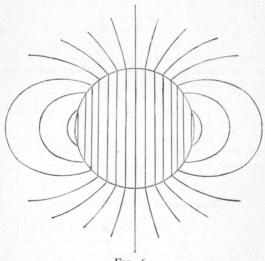

Fig. 6.

The variation in the intensity of the field, as well as in its direction, in the space round a uniformly magnetized sphere, can be found with the aid of the theory of the magnetic potential. This theory was developed by Laplace, Poisson and others, in the eighteenth and nineteenth centuries, on foundations already laid down (for the gravitational field) by Newton. Gauss applied the theory to the earth's magnetic field. He found that, as Gilbert had realized, the field of a uniformly magnetized sphere is an excellent first approximation to the earth's field, and he showed how to determine the field of this type that most closely fits the earth's field. This part of the field may be called the *regular* field of the earth, and the remainder the irregular field. Gauss showed how this also might be expressed in mathematical terms, and within the limits of accuracy then attainable he proved that both this and the regular field have their origin within the earth. Thus he confirmed Gilbert's conclusion, and extended it to the irregular part of the field.

THE FIELD OF A UNIFORMLY MAGNETIZED SPHERE.

Consider a uniformly magnetized sphere with centre O, radius *a*, and intensity of magnetization J. Its magnetic moment M is given by

$$\text{M} = \frac{4}{3}\pi a^3 \text{ J}.$$

The diameter along the direction of magnetization is called the *magnetic axis*, and its two ends are called the magnetic poles ; the one to which the north-seeking end of an ordinary compass needle is attracted is called the north pole, and the other the south pole.

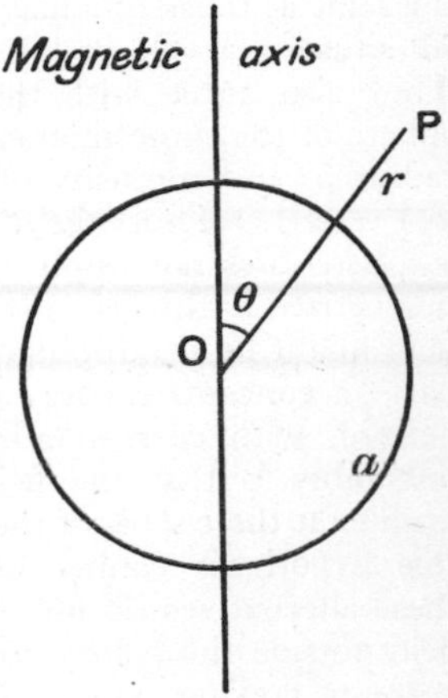

Let P (Fig. 7) be any point *outside the sphere ;* let *r* denote the distance OP, and θ the angle $(0 < \theta < \pi)$ between OP and the magnetic axis. The magnetic potential (Ω) at P is given by

FIG. 7.

$$\Omega = -\frac{\text{M} \cos \theta}{r^2}.$$

The inward radial component of force, corresponding to the terrestrial magnetic element Z, is $\partial\Omega/\partial r$. The component perpendicular to the radius, in the direction of decreasing θ, is $\partial\Omega/r\partial\theta$; it corresponds to the terrestrial magnetic element H. Clearly

$$Z = \frac{\partial\Omega}{\partial r} = \frac{2M\cos\theta}{r^3}, \quad H = \frac{\partial\Omega}{r\partial\theta} = \frac{M\sin\theta}{r^3}.$$

The angle of dip I and the intensity F are therefore given by

$$\tan I = Z/H = 2\cot\theta,$$
$$F = \frac{M}{r^3}(1 + 3\cos^2\theta).$$

The potential Ω, and the field outside the sphere, are the same as those of a magnetic particle of the same moment M situated at O, and directed along the magnetic axis. They also agree with those for any concentric magnetic sphere of the same moment, that is, any sphere of different radius a' and intensity of magnetization J', but such that $a'^3J' = a^3J$. Thus the existence of such a field outside a sphere does not imply that the sphere itself is uniformly magnetized; this is only one possible way in which the field might be produced; another possibility is that only a part—a concentric core—of the sphere is uniformly magnetized, with correspondingly greater intensity. A third possibility is that the field is due to a small but strong magnet at the centre of the sphere; in the case of the earth this hypothesis cannot be considered a likely one. But these alternatives do not exhaust the possibilities, since the field outside the sphere may be due to a system of electric currents flowing within, instead of to magnetized matter.

The formulæ for H, Z and F show that the intensity of the field and its components decreases outwards inversely as the *cube* of the distance from O. Hence the earth's magnetic field must die away much more rapidly than its gravitational field, whose intensity falls off only as the inverse *square* of the radius. (The irregular part of the earth's field decreases still more rapidly—see p. 23—so that the greater the distance from the earth, the more " regular " is the field ; that is, except in so far as the field is modified by electric currents in the space above the earth ; see p. 21, also p. 57).

Unlike the intensity, the direction of the magnetic force does not vary with the distance along a radius, since the dip I depends only on θ. This conclusion may be expected to apply approximately to the earth's field.

The formulæ for H and Z may be rewritten in the form

$$H = H_0 \frac{a^3}{r^3} \sin \theta, \quad Z = Z_0 \frac{a^3}{r^3} \cos \theta,$$

where $\qquad H_0 = \dfrac{M}{a^3} = \dfrac{4}{3}\pi J, \quad Z_0 = 2H_0,$

so that conversely

$$M = a^3 H_0, \quad J = \frac{3}{4\pi} H_0.$$

On the surface of the sphere $(r = a)$, H and Z are given by

$$H = H_0 \sin \theta, \quad Z = Z_0 \cos \theta.$$

Clearly Z_0 is the surface value of Z at the north pole $(\theta = 0)$; Z varies as $\cos \theta$, from Z_0 at this pole, through zero along the circle $\theta = 90°$, to $- Z_0$ at the south pole. The circle $\theta = 90°$, along which Z (and the dip I) vanishes, is called the magnetic equator of the sphere. H_0 is the surface value of H on the equator ; H decreases from this maximum value, proportionately to $\sin \theta$, to zero at the poles. The maximum (polar) value of Z, namely Z_0, is twice the maximum (equatorial) value H_0 of H. This is approximately true for the earth, since Z_0 and H_0 are (roughly) $0 \cdot 6\varGamma$ and $0 \cdot 3\varGamma$.

The surface equatorial value of H on a uniformly magnetized sphere is $\dfrac{4}{3}\pi J$. The corresponding value at the surface of a sphere of radius a, of which only an inner

2

concentric core of radius a' is magnetized, to intensity J', is M/a^3, where M is now $\frac{4}{5}\pi a'^3 J'$; hence H_0 is $\frac{4}{3}\pi(a'/a)^3 J'$.

The polar equation of the lines of force of a uniformly magnetized sphere is $r = c \sin^2 \theta$, where c is a constant, different for different lines. If the equation is written in the form

$$\frac{r}{a} = \frac{\sin^2 \theta}{\sin^2 \theta_0},$$

the new constant θ_0 represents the value of θ at which the line meets the sphere $(r = a)$. The maximum distance of this line from the sphere is attained when $\theta = 90°$, that is, above the magnetic equator, where $r = a/\sin^2 \theta_0$. For example, if $\theta_0 = 30°$, $a/\sin^2 \theta_0 = 4a$, corresponding to a height $3a$ above the equator.

NUMERICAL DATA FOR THE EARTH'S FIELD

The regular field of closest fit to the earth's field is found by a mathematical process known as the method of spherical harmonic analysis. This regular field has its north pole at approximately 78° N., 69° W., and its south pole at the opposite point on the earth, namely 78° S., 249° W. The north pole, which attracts the north-seeking end of a magnetic needle, is itself of the same polarity as a south-seeking end. The diameter joining the south to the north pole is called the earth's magnetic axis; it is inclined at 12° to the geographical axis. Its two ends are called the *axis-poles* of the earth's field, to distinguish them from the dip-poles (p. 3), where $H = 0$. On a uniformly magnetized sphere the dip-poles and the axis poles are identical; but this is not so for the earth's field, because of the presence of the additional " irregular " field, whose horizontal component does not happen to vanish at the axis-poles. Since the part of H due to the regular field is small near the axis-poles, an irregular field of low intensity can cause a considerable shift in the position of the point where the combined H is zero. The actual distance between the northern axis-pole and dip-pole is about 600 miles, while for the southern poles it is about 900 miles. The line joining the two dip-poles does not pass through the earth's centre O; it passes O at a distance of about 700 miles.

From the standpoint of geophysics the axis-poles are more significant than the dip-poles; but for seamen and others who may use the compass, in high latitudes, the dip-poles have the greater importance.

If the irregular part of the earth's field were absent, the lines of equal H, Z, F and I would all be circles centred on the magnetic axis. They would in fact coincide with the circles of *magnetic latitude*, this being defined as $90° - \theta$, where θ is the angular distance from the north axis-pole; θ itself is called the (magnetic) *colatitude*. The isomagnetic maps for these elements, if drawn on a Mercator projection based on the magnetic instead of the geographical axis, would show simply a series of lines parallel with the (magnetic) equator. On the usual Mercator projection relative to the geographical axis, the isomagnetic lines would be curves, but still quite simple and regular. The existence of the irregular field modifies their form, and creates a distinction between the four sets of curves; for example, the magnetic equator $(I = o = Z)$ is not a line of constant H or F.

If the regular field were alone present, the declination would be westerly over the hemisphere bounded by the meridians through the magnetic poles and containing England, and easterly over the other hemisphere. But the isogonic lines would not be simple; this is because the deviation of the magnetic from the geographical axis involves the existence of four isogonic foci (see p. 3), situated at the two dip-poles and the two geographical poles.

The meridian circles or planes passing through the magnetic axis poles are called the *magnetic meridians* or magnetic meridian planes.

The value of H_0 for the regular part of the earth's field (1922) is 0.316Γ; it corresponds to a magnetic moment

M ($M = a^3 H_0$, where a may be taken as 6370 km. or
$6\cdot37 \cdot 10^8$ cm.) of amount $8\cdot19 \cdot 10^{25}$. This is called the
magnetic moment of the earth. The intensity of mag-
netization J which the earth would have, if its regular
field were due to uniform magnetization throughout,
is $3H_0/4\pi$ or $0\cdot075$. The surface layers are on the average
certainly not magnetized to this extent.

The above value of H_0 refers to the epoch 1922. Earlier
determinations are as follows :

1829	Erman-Petersen	.	.	.	$0\cdot327$
1830	Gauss	.	.	.	$0\cdot331$
1845	Adams	.	.	.	$0\cdot328$
1880	Adams	.	.	.	$0\cdot324$
1880	Neumayer	.	.	.	$0\cdot323$
1885	Schmidt	.	.	.	$0\cdot324$
1885	Fritsche	.	.	.	$0\cdot322$
1922	Dyson and Furner	.	.	.	$0\cdot316$

Though the earlier determinations may be somewhat in
error, these results certainly indicate a decrease of a few
per cent. in H_0 and the earth's magnetic moment during
the last century (p. 11). When the great scale of the
phenomenon is considered, this must seem a remarkably
large and rapid secular change, not paralleled for any other
world-wide geophysical property.

The Irregular Part of the Earth's Field

The irregular part of the earth's field can be represented
graphically by " *iso-anomalous* " maps (showing the lines
along which each of its elements has a constant value)
and in other ways. In some parts of the world it contributes a substantial percentage to one or other component of the field, even apart from areas of special local
disturbance. It can also be expressed mathematically,
with the aid of an addition Ω' to the regular potential
function Ω (given, with reference to the earth's magnetic
axis, on p. 15).

The surface value of Ω', denoted by Ω_0', is expressible as a series of functions of geographical latitude (l) and longitude (λ, reckoned east from Greenwich). That is

$$\Omega_0' = C_2 a S_2 (l, \lambda) + C_3 a S_3 (l, \lambda) + \cdots,$$

where C_2, C_3 are constants and S_2, S_3, $\ldots$ are certain "surface harmonic" functions of l and λ, of "degree" $2, 3, \ldots$. The series does not start with suffix $_1$ because the term $C_1 S_1 (l, \lambda)$ would correspond to the regular part of the field. The north and east horizontal components of the irregular field, X', Y', are related to Ω_0' by the equations

$$X' = - \frac{\partial \Omega_0'}{a \partial l}, \qquad Y' = - \frac{\partial \Omega_0'}{a \cos l \partial \lambda}.$$

The coefficients C, and the precise form of the functions S, including C_1 and S_1, are found by an analysis of the observed distribution of *either* X *or* Y over the earth's surface. The expressions thus separately found agree substantially, but not exactly. The small difference may be due to three causes, namely, (1) errors in the observed data, (2) incompleteness of the analysis, (3) the existence of a part of the field which does not possess a potential.

THE NON-POTENTIAL FIELD : MAGNETIC LINE INTEGRALS

The presence of a *non-potential field* would imply the existence of electric currents flowing across the earth's surface, from air to earth or *vice versa*. Another way in which the existence of such currents could be detected magnetically would be by the calculation of line integrals of the horizontal magnetic force round closed curves on the earth's surface ; the value of such a line integral should be $4\pi i$, where i is the total electric current flowing through the circuit. If the circuit is a circle of latitude, for example, the line integral is simply $\int Y \, ds$ or $\int H \sin D \, ds$ taken all round the circle. Such line-integrals as have been calculated do not exactly vanish ; this may be partly due to errors in the magnetic data, but it is doubtful whether such errors can completely account for the non-vanishing of the line integrals. The difficulty in crediting the reality of the earth-air currents indicated by the line integrals is their magnitude ; this is of the order 10^{-12} ampere per sq. cm., outwards over some areas and inwards over others. This current-intensity is 10^4 times as great as the earth-air currents measured by the ordinary methods of atmospheric electricity. The elucidation of this discrepancy between the magnetic and electric results must await more accurate magnetic measurements. For the present the possibility must remain open, that an appreciable part of the magnetic field near the earth's surface —not more than 3 per cent. of the whole—may be due to earth-air currents, and not possess a potential.

THE EXTERNAL PART OF THE EARTH'S FIELD

Subject to a slight uncertainty due to a possible non-potential field, the expressions for Ω_0' (p. 21) found separately from the north and east components of horizontal force are in agreement with one another. If the field were wholly of internal origin, the potential Ω' of the irregular field, at any point above the earth's surface, would be given by

$$\Omega' = \frac{a^4}{r^3} C_2 S_2 (l, \lambda) + \frac{a^5}{r^4} C_3 S_3 (l, \lambda) + \ldots ;$$

the corresponding value of Z', the inward radial component of the irregular field, would be given by

$$Z' = \frac{\partial \Omega'}{\partial r} = - 3\left(\frac{a}{r}\right)^4 C_2 S_2 - 4\left(\frac{a}{r}\right)^5 C_3 S_3 + \ldots,$$

so that at the earth's surface $(r = a)$,

$$Z' = - 3C_2 S_2 - 4C_3 S_3 - \ldots.$$

The observed distribution of Z' is found to agree substantially, but not exactly, with the expression thus obtained from the independent measurements of X' and Y'.

The small discrepancy may be due either to errors in the three sets of data (X', Y', Z'), or to the existence, in the field near the earth's surface, of a small part due to external causes. The potential of this part would be expressible in the form

$$\frac{r^2}{a} C_2'' S_2' + \frac{r^3}{a^2} C_3'' S_3'' + \cdots,$$

and the corresponding part of Z' by

$$2\frac{r}{a} C_2'' S_2'' + 3\frac{r^2}{a^2} C_3'' S_3'' + \cdots,$$

or, at the surface, by

$$2C_2'' S_2'' + 3 C_3'' S_3'' + \cdots.$$

Owing to the difference between this and the preceding expression for Z' (corresponding to an internal field) it is possible to determine the internal and external parts of Ω', and therefore of the irregular field (apart from any non-potential part).

With the data at present available, the possibility is left open that a small part of the field near the earth's surface, not more than about 3 per cent. of the whole, may be of external origin, due to electric currents flowing somewhere above the earth's surface. Thus, allowing for a possible non-potential part of similar magnitude, we may say that at least 94 per cent. of the field has a potential, and is of internal origin. The components of the successive harmonic terms in the irregular part of the field decrease outwards proportionately to $1/r^4$, $1/r^5$, $\cdots$. Hence, apart from the uncertainty due to the non-potential and external parts of the field, the importance of the irregular field relative to the regular field must steadily decrease outwards.

THE UPWARD DECREASE OF THE EARTH'S FIELD

The upward decrease in the earth's field is thus approximately as a^3/r^3, or, writing $r = a + h$, as $(1 + h/a)^{-3}$.

For small heights this is $1 - 3h/a$; if h is measured in kilometres, any component will be decreased by a fraction $h/2123$ of itself at height h. For example, at the equator the horizontal force $(\cdot3\varGamma)$ will decrease by about 14γ in 1 kilometre. This is too small to measure in the ordinary way, since accurate magnetic measurements cannot be made in balloons, while mountain and valley observations may not be comparable, owing to field-irregularities due to the mountains themselves. Certain radio measurements, however, depend on the magnetic field at the level of the ionized layers in the upper atmosphere, at heights of 200 km. or more : there the expected reduction of the field is of the order 10 per cent., and the radio measures actually indicate such a decrease.

Other phenomena that depend on the earth's magnetic field outside the earth, at still greater distances, are the *aurora polaris* and the cosmic rays. Both are due to electrified particles coming from afar, in the former case from the sun and in the latter from the depths of space. When they approach the earth, while still at a distance of many earth-radii, they are deflected by its magnetic field, which diverts them preferentially to high magnetic latitudes.

THE TECHNICAL IMPORTANCE OF THE EARTH'S MAGNETIC FIELD

The most widespread and the earliest technical application of the earth's magnetic field is to navigation, depending on the directive action of the field upon the compass needle. This use has now extended to aerial navigation. Another application of almost equal importance and long standing is to surveying, both on the surface and in mines. All these applications depend, for their full development, on the existence of isogonic charts of recent date, in order that true bearings may be obtained from magnetic bearings by correction for the magnetic declination.

Another important economic application of the earth's

field relates to the search for valuable minerals or oilfields. In many cases such deposits produce or are associated with local disturbances in the earth's magnetic field. The observation of such disturbances, by instruments specially constructed for the purpose, is often helpful in locating valuable mine or oil fields : the results are usually interpreted in conjunction with geological data or with geophysical measurements of other kinds.

The earth's magnetism influences practical affairs in other ways : it affects the propagation of radio waves. At times of disturbance of the magnetic field (cf. Chapter II) it may seriously affect long distance transmission. Moreover, at such times it often hinders cable telegraphy.

THE ROTATION OF THE EARTH'S FIELD

The field of an elementary magnet consisting of two equal and opposite poles m, $- m$ at closely neighbouring points P, P' has axial symmetry about the line P'P. There is no meaning in the phrase the rotation of the magnet about P'P, if the poles are regarded as mathematical points. If the magnet is moved in a circle about an axis O'O *parallel* to P'P it may be said to revolve round O'O ; but its motion is still one of translation and not of rotation, and its field also must be thought of as translated and not rotated. A magnet always directed *perpendicular* to O'O, and carried round in the same circle, would, however, be in rotation as well as in translation, and its field would share this rotation.

The earth's field could be produced by a collection of small magnets distributed somewhere in its interior : whether these magnets are particles or electromagnets—due to electrons circling around nuclei or flowing in ordinary current circuits—they may be thought of as resolved into components respectively parallel and perpendicular to the earth's axis of rotation. The fields of the axial component magnets are translated but not rotated with the earth ; the fields of the transverse components are rotated as well as translated. The distinction may, however, be disregarded for all ordinary purposes; the inequalities in the earth's field travel round with it in its diurnal rotation.

The Cause of the Earth's Magnetism and its Secular Variation

It has been seen (pp. 16-20) that the earth's regular field might be due to a uniform distribution of magnetization of intensity 0·075 throughout its volume, or to a uniform distribution of intensity $k^3 \times 0·075$ throughout a concentric core of radius smaller in the ratio $1/k$ ($k > 1$). The surface layers are not magnetized (on the average) to the intensity 0·075, and on account of the progressive downward increase of temperature, the earth's substance seems unlikely to be magnetizable at all below a very moderate depth. It has been thought that the associated downward increase of pressure might *raise* the limiting temperature above which the power of retaining magnetization is lost, thus preserving the magnetizability to somewhat greater depths; but experiments have not confirmed this supposition—the pressure having a slightly contrary effect. However, the pressures attained deep within the earth far transcend those with which it is at present possible to experiment in the laboratory. Hence we cannot exclude the possibility that in or above the earth's metallic liquid core the material is magnetizable, and may in this way be responsible for the earth's field: whether or not this is actually the cause of the field must for the present remain a matter merely for conjecture.

The field may, on the other hand, be due to a system of electric currents flowing within the earth, around the earth's axis. This is likewise a pure speculation. The question of the prior cause arises in either case: we do not know how either magnetization, or electric currents, could originate in the course of the earth's history. If there are such electric currents, however, and if they are not continuously maintained, they would slowly decay owing to the electrical resistance of the earth. The time of decay would depend on the electrical resistivity of the material traversed by the currents ; we have some information (pp. 52-55) about the resistance within the earth, but it relates only to a depth that is small compared with the earth's radius. Below that depth (perhaps a tenth of the radius) we have little positive knowledge, and the great pressures place the physical state of the matter beyond our experience. It is known, however, that the time of decay of a system of currents of given type, in material of given resistance, is proportional to the linear size of the system ; hence it may be very long for a body so large as the earth. An alternative suggestion has been made that the electric current system, instead of freely decaying, may be continuously maintained by electro-magnetic induction ; convective motion in the liquid core, in meridian planes, might, in conjunction with the magnetic field, be able to induce electromotive forces such as would balance the resistance losses. During the past century the earth's regular field actually seems to have decreased (p. 20), but only long continued observation can show whether this decrease corresponds to an exponential decay ; without this knowledge a decision between these alternative current-hypotheses must remain in suspense.

Other hypotheses of a more fundamental kind have been made, in the attempt to account for the earth's field as a consequence of the earth's rotation : for this purpose general properties of matter have been invoked, differing inappreciably from those already found by experiment, under the conditions and on the scale available in the laboratory, but sufficient, in the case of a body so large as the earth, to have magnetic results of the observed kind. Some care is necessary, in forming such hypotheses, to avoid demonstrably untrue consequences of other kinds. But theories devised *ad hoc*, to explain one particular phenomenon, are of comparatively little interest unless they are capable of predicting some other, unknown, consequence that can be tested by experiment. Success of this kind has not been achieved. Moreover, such theories can, by their very nature, account only for the component of the earth's magnetic moment along the geographical axis. The transverse component, to which is due the obliquity of the magnetic axis, is a substantial fraction of the axial component, and still requires explanation by further hypotheses. The same is true of the regional irregularities of the field.

The secular variation, like the main field, is also as yet quite mysterious and unexplained. It seems to imply considerable changes in the earth's interior, of which we have little other indication. Perhaps the most likely speculation is that there is some internal convection proceeding within the earth, at different rates or at different depths in different regions ; the motion may be supposed either to induce regional electric current systems, or, by changing the distribution of heterogeneously conducting material, to modify the path of existing electric current systems ; in either of these ways the regional irregularity of the secular magnetic variation might be accounted for.

CHAPTER II

THE TRANSIENT MAGNETIC VARIATIONS

The Sunspot Cycle; Sunspot Numbers

THE number and area of the spots on the sun vary, there being at times no spots, and at other times many. To each day there is assigned (at Zürich) a daily sunspot number characterizing the degree of spottedness of the sun on that day, taking into account both the number and the areas of the spots. The monthly and annual means of these daily numbers are called the monthly and annual mean sunspot numbers. The daily numbers vary somewhat irregularly : the monthly numbers naturally "run" more smoothly, and the annual means still more so. The latter clearly show a roughly periodic variation, the period being about eleven years from one "sunspot maximum" (or minimum) to the next (see Fig. 29, p. 102). The variation in the spottedness, from minimum to maximum and back to minimum again, is called the *solar* or *sunspot cycle*.

Quiet and Disturbed Days; Character Figures

The continuous magnetic records of any observatory show that on some days all the three elements undergo smooth and regular variations, while on others they are more or less disturbed. Days of the first kind are said to be magnetically *quiet* or *calm* (at that station) : days of the second kind are called magnetically *active* or *disturbed* days.

For many years an international scheme has been in operation by which, at each observatory, a figure 0, 1, or 2 is assigned to each Greenwich day (from midnight to midnight) according to the magnetic character of the day at that observatory. The figure 0 refers to conditions quieter, and the figure 2 to conditions more disturbed, than the average. The classification is generally made by simple inspection of the records of the three elements for the day ; thus it has no definite quantitative basis, and the standard of disturbance required for a figure is apt to be raised during periods of more than usual *activity* or *disturbance*, and to be lowered during quiet periods. The standard also varies from one observatory to another, according to the general level of disturbance at each.

The daily figures from all the co-operating observatories are sent to a central office (at de Bilt, Holland) where the average for each day is taken. The resulting figure, to one place of decimals, is called the *international magnetic character figure* for the day : of course it lies between 0·0 and 2·0.

It is found that, on the whole, the day-to-day changes in the intensity of disturbance follow a similar course over a wide area, and that days classified as 2 at one observatory are usually classified as 1 or 2 at others, and only rarely as 0 : likewise quiet conditions are usually widespread.

On the basis of these international character figures, the central office selects five of the quietest and five of the most disturbed days in each calendar month ; these are called the *international quiet* or *disturbed* days.

Attempts are being made to improve the daily classification, or to replace it by one based on a more quantitative method. But the figures obtained by the simple method described have proved of great value in many types of magnetic investigation.

THE THREE MAIN TRANSIENT VARIATIONS : S, D and L

The degree of magnetic activity varies from day to day over a wide range, and few days seem wholly free from disturbance. But, except in periods of extreme activity, it is quite evident that the disturbance is superposed on a *regular daily variation*. This may be called the solar daily variation, to distinguish it from another regular daily variation which the magnetic field is found to undergo, depending on lunar time. For brevity it is convenient to refer to these two daily variations by the letters S (solar) and L (lunar). The former is seen in its pure form on quiet days, and it is convenient then to denote it by S_q. The letter D may likewise be used to refer to magnetic disturbance.* These three variations, S, L and D, together with the secular variation, comprise the most important of the changes in the earth's magnetic field. Since S, D and L, unlike the secular variation, produce no large and long enduring change in the earth's field, they may be called the *transient* magnetic variations.

There is one important distinction between S and D on the one hand, and L on the other : the former can be recognized at sight from the magnetographs, whereas L cannot, because it is of much smaller range ; it can be determined only by averaging over many days. But its small magnitude does not detract from its great theoretical interest and significance.

Each element is affected in a characteristic way by each of the three types of variation S, L and D. Hence a single observatory provides material for nine separate investigations—on the nature of S, D and L in each of the three magnetic elements.

The results of such studies from a number of observatories widely distributed in latitude and longitude must be collated and synthesized, if a comprehensive understanding of the phenomena is to be gained. For completeness this work should be done not only for S, L and D as determined from the mean of one or more years, but also for each season separately, because both their type and their range are found to vary in the course of each year. Moreover,

---

* The same symbol is used for the magnetic declination, but there seems little fear of confusion on this account.

their range, and the incidence of D, vary from year to year, requiring a further extension of the investigation, for different years. The study of the transient magnetic variations is thus a complex, laborious and extensive task. The description and concise representation of the leading facts, when found, is also somewhat difficult. Only gradually, over a long period of time, have suitable methods of representation and investigation been evolved—methods which are likely to be of great value also in allied fields of geophysical study that have been more recently developed.

OBSERVATORY DATA

It is customary at magnetic observatories to measure the value of each element *hourly*. Before photographic registration was introduced, this was done by eye readings, but it is now done from the magnetographs. The measurement may be of the value at an instant, but this has the drawback that a chance disturbance may make an instantaneous value unrepresentative of the value of the element at neighbouring times. Hence at many observatories the practice is to measure the mean values of the elements for hourly intervals. Usually these intervals extend *from* one exact hour *to* the next, but at some observatories intervals *centred* at such exact hours are used instead.

The *time-reckoning* to which these hourly measures refer may be the local time of the observatory, or the standard zone time for the region in which it is situated (that is, time differing by a whole number of hours from Greenwich mean time).

In any case, successive hourly values of each element are obtained and tabulated. Where hour-to-hour means are used, the mean of the 24 values for each day, covering the period from midnight (0^h) to the following midnight (24^h), is called the *daily mean* value. Where instantaneous values are measured, or hourly means centred at exact hours, the daily mean is the average of the 24 values consisting of the measures for the hours 1 to 23, together with the mean of those for o and 24; the measures for o^h and 24^h usually differ, and the difference $(24^h)-(o^h)$ is called the *non-cyclic* or *non-periodic variation* for the day. Where hour-to-hour means are used, this non-periodic variation can be measured by

$$\tfrac{1}{2}\{(24\tfrac{1}{2}) + (23\tfrac{1}{2}) - (o\tfrac{1}{2}) - (-\,o\tfrac{1}{2})\},$$

where the figures in brackets refer to the hourly means centred at the epochs indicated. The non-periodic variation of course includes a part due to the secular variation, but in a single day this is quite insignificant.

Many observatories publish for each day the *absolute maxima* and *minima* of each element (sometimes giving also the times at which they occur), or, alternatively, the difference between them, which is the *absolute daily range* for the day; it may be denoted by R, with suffix H, D, V for the element concerned. This usually exceeds R' (with the same suffix), defined as the range of the *tabulated hourly values* for the day. In connection with some investigations the *hourly range*, or range during each hour, is considered: it may be denoted by r, with suffixes for the hour and element concerned.

Besides the mean of the hourly values for each day (i.e. the daily mean), many observatory year-books give the mean of the hourly values for each hour, for all the days of each month, and often also for selected groups of days (usually the international five quietest and five most disturbed days). The sequence of mean hourly values thus obtained indicates the mean daily variation for the month (or for the selected days in the month). The sequence may contain 24 or 25 values; in the latter case it may refer to the hours o^h to 24^h, or $o\tfrac{1}{2}^h$ to $24\tfrac{1}{2}^h$; the difference between the last and first gives the mean non-periodic variation for the month or group of days.

The mean of the daily mean values for the month (or year) is called the *monthly* (or *annual*) *mean* value; group mean values may likewise be formed from the daily means for groups of selected days. When the monthly or group

3

mean value is subtracted from the corresponding sequence of hourly means which gives the daily variation, a sequence of *hourly departures* from the mean is obtained ; this is called the *mean daily inequality* for the month or group of days. If these departures are plotted against the time, the curve or graph obtained is called the *daily variation curve* for the element. The daily inequality (and its graph) obtained from the five quietest days per month may be taken as fairly representing S_q (p. 31) except for months in which even these days show appreciable disturbance. It is true that S_q thus determined includes also the secular variation and the lunar daily variation ; these can be allowed for if desired, but they are usually so small that this is considered unnecessary.

THE ANNUAL VARIATION OF THE MAGNETIC ELEMENTS

The monthly mean values of the magnetic elements show very little systematic variation throughout the year, when the secular variation has been allowed for. Thus the elements have scarcely any *annual variation*, such as is shown by many meteorological elements—especially the air temperature and, in some regions (such as Siberia), the barometric pressure.

S_q, S_d, AND S_D

Except at stations in high latitudes, and except in months including especially great disturbance, the mean daily variation S obtained from all days of a month does not differ much from S_q, the mean daily variation obtained from quiet days. Even when S is derived from a set of ordinarily disturbed days, such as the five most disturbed days per month (in which case it may be denoted by S_d), it does not differ very greatly from S_q except in high latitudes, provided that the average is formed from many days (that is, from five days each from many months) in order to eliminate the irregularities associated with individual periods of disturbance.

This similarity between S_q and S or S_d implies that average days, and ordinarily disturbed days, differ from quiet days mainly through irregular variations that nearly average out, at each hour, in the mean of a number of days —so long as attention is confined to low and middle latitudes. But the disturbance does not quite average out: there *is* a systematic difference between S_q, and S or S_d; it can be represented by a sequence of hourly differences. This sequence may be denoted by $S - S_q$, when the hourly departures for *quiet* days are subtracted from those for *all* days; or by $S_d - S_q$, when the hourly departures for quiet days are subtracted from those for *disturbed* days. Both $S - S_q$ and $S_d - S_q$ are due to disturbance, the average intensity being greater in the latter case; this part of the disturbance, being a solar daily variation, may conveniently be denoted by S_D, and called the *disturbance daily variation*. On average days S_q is combined with S_D in small intensity to give S, while on disturbed days S_q is combined with S_D in decidedly greater intensity.

D, S_D, D_m, D_{st} AND D_i

Disturbance in middle and low latitudes consists largely of irregular variations, but includes a portion which is systematically related to the time of day, namely the part S_D just defined. If we could separate the disturbance changes from the others that are simultaneously proceeding (due to S_q, L and the secular variation) and then subtract from the disturbance changes this systematic part S_D, the difference would be found not wholly irregular. There is in fact a part of D which modifies the daily mean value of the elements, so as to decrease H and increase V. This can be found by subtracting the mean values of the elements on quiet days from those for all days or disturbed days; the difference is in the same sense in the two cases, but greater for the disturbed than for the all-day difference, as would be expected. The part of D which corresponds to this average change in the mean value of the elements may be denoted by D_m; it is on the average the daily mean of a part of D, which may be denoted by D_{st}, that depends on " storm-time " (p. 76). When not only S_D but also D_{st} is subtracted from D, the remainder appears to be quite irregular, and may be denoted by D_i.

THE DEPENDENCE OF S_q AND S_D ON LOCAL TIME

One fortunate regularity in the great mass of facts about S_q and S_D is that, at a given epoch, these daily variations depend mainly on latitude and local time, and not also on longitude. The same applies to L relative to local lunar time. This means that they are substantially the same at all the stations round any circle of latitude, at corresponding local times. There is probably less difference, for example, in the daily variation of H at different points along the equator than there is between the daily variation of air temperature at continental and oceanic stations on the equator.

These remarks apply particularly to middle and low latitudes ; in high latitudes the obliquity of the magnetic axis makes the longitude more significant, but even there the daily variations seem to be nearly the same, at corresponding local times, at stations in the same *magnetic* latitude (p. 19).

Thus S_q and S_D, at any given epoch, depend on two variables, latitude l and local time t, instead of on three, namely, l, t and the longitude λ. Hence each of these two types of daily variation can be illustrated by one set of curves for each element, showing the daily variations experienced in a series of latitudes, on a local-time scale of abscissæ.

THE GEOGRAPHICAL DISTRIBUTION OF THE S_q AND S_D FIELDS

The daily magnetic variations S_q and S_D, as also the lunar daily variation L, and the parts of D, namely D_m (or D_{st}) and D_i, can usefully be thought of as due to independent magnetic fields superposed on the main field and on each other. The S_q and S_D fields, and also the L field, are specified at each place and time by the corresponding departures of the three elements from their mean values; similarly for D_m, D_{st} and D_i. The D_i field may be expected to have an irregular geographical distribution, changing irregularly with the time; the other fields, of S_q, S_D, L and D_m (or D_{st}), may be expected to show more regularity and simplicity. It is of course difficult to visualize vector fields, especially when they are changing with the time. But the fact that S_q, S_D and L depend on latitude and local (solar or lunar) time, and are independent of the longitude, helps greatly in forming a mental picture of these fields. This can be explained most simply by considering some single geophysical property which depends on the local (solar) time, such as air temperature or any one magnetic element (instead of considering the vector quantity,

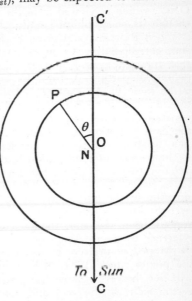

FIG. 8.

magnetic force, which has three components). It will also suffice, to convey the idea involved, if we consider the equinoctial epochs, in March and September, when the earth's axis ON is perpendicular to the line joining its centre O to the centre C of the sun. Let P denote any point on the earth, in some latitude l. As the earth revolves, P describes a circle round the axis ON. The local time at

P signifies the angle, in time reckoning (24 hours being equivalent to 360°) between the meridian half-plane ONP through P, and the meridian half-plane ONC′ opposite to that containing C ; this is indicated by θ in Fig. 8, in which the earth is supposed to be viewed along its axis, looking toward the north pole. Thus the local time at P is simply the longitude of P relative to the half-plane ONC′, which as viewed from the sun is a fixed half-plane, though its geographical longitude varies continuously.

When P attains any given position as viewed from the sun, corresponding to any given local time, we suppose that the geophysical property we are considering has a definite departure Δ from its mean value, and that Δ is the same for all stations in latitude l, at the same local time θ : this is what is meant when we say that the daily variation depends only on l and the local time. Thus the daily variation in latitude l may be considered either as a variation with time at each station, or as corresponding to the passage of each station through a series of positions (relative to the meridian half-plane ONC or ONC′) each characterized by a particular value of Δ. Viewing the situation in the latter way, we picture a distribution of Δ over the earth, a distribution depending on l and θ, fixed as viewed from the sun, though continuously varying with reference to the rotating earth. The distribution of Δ can be mapped, if desired, by means of contour lines through the points where Δ has given values; the map so formed will not, however, show the geographical features of the earth, such as the seas and continents, since these are continually shifting relative to the distribution of Δ, or, as one may prefer to say, the Δ distribution is continually varying relative to the earth, rotating round the axis, ON, as the sun itself appears to do.

This way of considering the daily variation of Δ is merely a helpful way of picturing it, and if desired, of mapping it, as a whole ; it implies no hypothesis as to the way in which the variation is produced. It substitutes the conception of the rotation of the earth within a Δ-distribution fixed relative to the sun, that is, a constant Δ-distribution, for the conception of a time-variation at numberless points of the earth. The Δ-distribution, while regarded as sensibly constant during a single day, may of course be supposed to change slowly with the seasons.

The simplest geophysical property that can be viewed in the above way is that of daylight or darkness. The hemisphere facing the sun is lit up (sunlit) while the opposite hemisphere is dark so far as direct sunlight is concerned. Each point P in any latitude undergoes the daily variation of light and darkness, as it traverses its path round the axis, from the dark to the sunlit hemisphere and back again to darkness.

Another simple property that undergoes a daily variation roughly depending on local time is the air temperature. This corresponds to a distribution of temperature approximately fixed as viewed from the sun, the temperature being higher over the sunlit hemisphere than over the dark hemisphere. In this case, however, the temperature distribution is not strictly constant as viewed from the sun, but changes somewhat according to the part of the earth (land or sea) presented to the sun : that is, the daily variation depends on geographical longitude as well as on local time.

Likewise the S_q and S_D daily variations may be thought of as indicating the existence of two magnetic fields, distributed in certain definite ways, constant as viewed from the sun. No attempt need be made, however, at this stage to form definite pictures of these fields : this will be considered later (p. 58).

THE D FIELD

Magnetic disturbance may be regarded as indicating the superposition of an additional transient magnetic (D) field upon the main field and the S_q field. The D field will include the S_D field, which in fact is the part of D that has a regular dependence on the orientation of the earth relative to the sun. The rest of the D field can be divided into a part D_{st} which is symmetrical about the earth's axis, but which varies with time, both in form and intensity; and a remainder D_i which varies irregularly with the time, and is somewhat inconstant in its geographical distribution.

THE L FIELD

The lunar daily magnetic variation L is, in the main, dependent on lunar local time, that is, time reckoned from the hour at which the moon crosses the (upper or lower) meridian of each station. It can be regarded as due to the existence of a very weak magnetic (L) field which has a definite distribution over the earth, as viewed from the moon. But its distribution, as will appear (Chapter IV), is also much affected by the sun.

The first aim of the study of the magnetographs, drawn from many observatories, must be to ascertain the nature of these three fields, S_q, D, and L, *near the earth's surface*. This is a necessary step towards the further object of determining the distribution of the same fields elsewhere, within and above the earth: and towards the ultimate goal, the explanation of the physical causes or origins of these fields.

CHAPTER III

THE QUIET-DAY SOLAR DAILY MAGNETIC VARIATION S_q

DAILY VARIATION CURVES FOR S_q

THE material for the study of S_q consists essentially of the solar daily inequalities (p. 34) of the three elements, from a number of observatories, in different latitudes. These may be represented by curves, one for each element in each latitude considered. The ordinates are the departures of the element from its mean value, at different hours of local time. Such curves are given in the left-hand portions (a) of Figs. 9, 10, 11, for observatories, or groups of observatories, as follows :

(1) Sitka, magnetic latitude 60°.
(2) Pavlovsk, magnetic latitude 56°.
(3) Pola, Potsdam, Greenwich, mean magnetic latitude 51°.
(4) Zikawei, San Fernando, Cheltenham, Baldwin, 40°.
(5) Batavia, Porto Rico, Honolulu, 22°.

The curves refer to the mean of one or more years. For stations in southern latitude l, the curves for H are approximately the same as for northern latitude l, while for Z and for the declination they are reversed on crossing the equator. Thus the Z and declination curves may be expected to reduce to zero amplitude at the equator ; actually their reversal occurs through transitional stages not of zero amplitude.

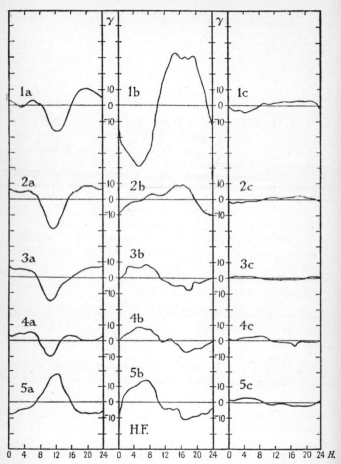

FIG. 9.—Quiet and disturbance daily variations in H (p. 41).

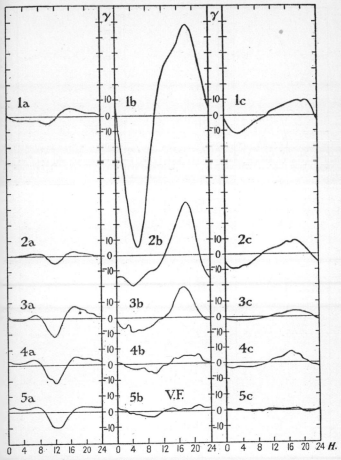

FIG. 10.—Quiet and disturbance daily variations in V (p. 41).

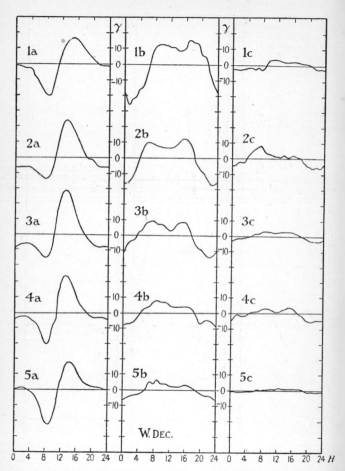

Fig. 11.—Quiet and disturbance daily variations in W. Dec. (p. 41).

The curves (b) and (c) in Figs. 9-11 represent S_D, derived from groups of days of different disturbance intensity. The curves (c) are derived from all days minus quiet days, and the curves (b) from days of considerably greater disturbance (less S_q). It is clear that, as stated on page 34, S_D is small compared with S_q on ordinary days, over the range of latitude $-50°$ to $+50°$, that is, for the curves (3) to (5); but in the case of V the curves 1(c) and 2(c), for magnetic latitudes 60° and 56°, have a greater range than 2(a).

VECTOR DIAGRAMS FOR S_q

Another method of representing S_q at any one station, which takes account of the vector character of the magnetic field or force F, is by means of a *vector diagram*. Let F be represented in direction and (on some chosen scale) in magnitude by a line O'P, where O' is a fixed origin; as F varies, the end P of the line O'P will move in space. If the mean position of P be O, then OP will represent the departure of F, at any time, from its mean value. In studying S, L and D we are mainly concerned with this departure OP, and not with the mean vector O'O, which usually far exceeds OP in length.

If we confine attention to that part of the magnetic variation which has a solar daily period, and, in particular, to S_q, the non-periodic variation having been allowed for, the point P daily describes a closed curve. It is convenient to imagine that the points of this closed curve that correspond to exact hours of local solar time are marked and numbered accordingly, so that not only the course but also the rate of the variation of F is indicated. This curve, with its origin O, constitutes what is called the magnetic vector diagram of S_q for the station considered. It is in general not a plane curve, and hence cannot be quite simply illustrated on flat paper; for this reason it is customary to consider its plane projections on either the horizontal or some vertical plane. The horizontal projection can be drawn by consideration of the S_q variations in H and D (declination) alone; the variations of H and Z similarly give the projection on the vertical plane passing through the compass direction at the point—the so-called magnetic meridian plane. Fig. 12 gives examples

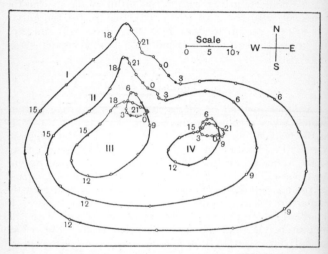

FIG. 12.—Quiet-day vector diagrams of the daily variation of magnetic force in the horizontal plane at Greenwich, 1889-1914.

      I. June, sunspot maximum years.
    II. June, sunspot minimum years.
  III. December, sunspot maximum years.
  IV. December, sunspot minimum years.

of horizontal vector diagrams for Greenwich. The larger curves refer to a summer month (June) and the smaller to a winter month (December). In these curves the part which is described during the hours of daylight is emphasized by being drawn especially thick.

THE CONTRAST BETWEEN THE DAY AND THE NIGHT CHANGES IN S_q

Such vector diagrams illustrate a notable feature of S_q, which can also be seen, though perhaps less readily, in the daily variation curves for the separate elements : namely, that the S_q variation is greater and more rapid during the hours of daylight than of darkness. It suggests that the S_q field is more intense and varied over the hemisphere of the earth that is turned towards the sun, than over the dark hemisphere. It implies not only that the sun is the ultimate cause of S_q, but also that the agent whereby the sun exerts its influence is something which, like the sun's heat and light rays, travels in straight lines from the sun and falls only, or mainly, on the side of the earth visible from the sun.

THE ANNUAL VARIATION OF S_q

Another notable feature of S_q, which confirms this view, is the annual variation of amplitude (as well as type) at stations in moderate and high latitudes. This is illustrated by the Fig. 12, which contrasts the summer (June) and winter (December) horizontal vector diagrams for Greenwich. Clearly S_q is much greater at that station in summer than in winter. Corresponding diagrams for other stations show generally that S_q is greater in proportion as the exposure of the station towards the sun, during the diurnal rotation of the earth, is more direct and prolonged.

In these respects S_q is like the daily variation of air temperature, which obviously depends on the reception of the sun's heat rays ; these are more direct, and are received for a larger fraction of the day in summer than in winter.

S_q AND THE SUNSPOT CYCLE.*

But S_q *differs* from the air-temperature variation in one important respect ; its amplitude is notably greater in

* See p. 29.

years of sunspot maximum (see p. 29) than of sunspot minimum; this also is indicated in Fig. 12, which gives both summer and winter curves for each type of year separately. The curves for sunspot maximum years are decidedly larger than those for minimum years. This remarkable fact not only emphasizes the conclusion that

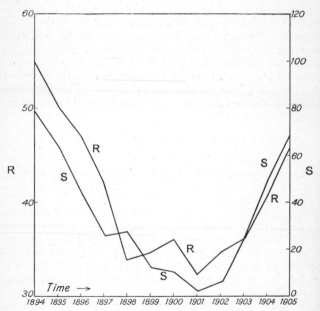

Fig. 13.—Mean quiet-day range (R) in H at Bombay, and annual mean sunspot numbers (s).

S_q is caused by the sun: it shows that the solar agent is not the heat and light radiation that we can directly measure; because the intensity of this radiation varies scarcely, if at all, in correspondence with the sunspot cycle.

The variation of S_q with the sunspot cycle can be illustrated also by comparing the variations, from year to year, in the range (R) of the annual mean S_q, with those of the annual mean sunspot numbers s (p. 29) as in Fig. 13.   In this figure R refers to the quiet-day variation of horizontal force at Bombay ; the period chosen is the eleven-year cycle 1894-1905.   It is clear that the variations of R and s, while not strictly parallel, are closely similar.   There is a wealth of evidence to the same effect, for other years, elements and stations.

These facts about S_q can be summarized by saying that the S_q field is more intense over the sunlit than over the dark hemisphere of the earth, and (at the solstices when the northern and southern hemispheres are unequally exposed to the sun's rays) over the summer than over the winter hemisphere : further, its intensity as a whole varies in correspondence with the sunspot cycle, being from 50 per cent. to 100 per cent. greater at sunspot maximum than at sunspot minimum.

THE DAY-TO-DAY VARIABILITY OF S_q

Yet another interesting and important characteristic of S_q is its variation of range from day to day ; this appears to be independent of any admixture of S_D or other effect of disturbance, since it is shown even when only the quietest days are considered.   After fully allowing for the regular annual variation of range (and also for the year-to-year variation of range connected with the solar cycle), the range is found to vary irregularly from day to day. It is shown particularly well when groups of several suc- cessive very quiet days, such as occur fairly often (especi- ally in sunspot minimum years), are examined.   The variations of range are not proportionate for different elements even at the same station, nor for the same ele- ments at different stations : there is, however, a correlation, sometimes considerable and sometimes very small, but apparently always positive, between the changes of range in different elements and for the same or different stations. If the range everywhere and in all elements varied from

day to day in the same ratio, it would correspond to a change
in the intensity, without change in the " form " of the S_q
field : the actual changes of ratio show that the field varies
somewhat in form as well as in intensity.

THE MATHEMATICAL REPRESENTATION OF S_q

For some purposes it is of value to express S_q in mathematical terms. The first stage in this process is to make
a harmonic or " Fourier " analysis of the daily variation
curve or inequality for each magnetic element at each
magnetic observatory. The curve is thus represented as
the sum of a number of simple sine or cosine waves,
periodic in the day or in simple fractions of the day ($\frac{1}{2}$, $\frac{1}{3}$, $\frac{1}{4}$,
. . .) ; the mathematical expression of the departure from
the mean at the local time t is of the form :

$$\begin{aligned}
\Sigma(a_n \cos nt &+ b_n \sin nt) \\
= a_1 \cos t &+ b_1 \sin t \\
+ a_2 \cos 2t &+ b_2 \sin 2t \\
+ a_3 \cos 3t &+ b_3 \sin 3t \\
+ a_4 \cos 4t &+ b_4 \sin 4t.
\end{aligned}$$

The first two terms ($n = 1$) represent the part periodic
in a whole solar day ; this is called the "*diurnal component*." The next two terms ($n = 2$) give the semi-
diurnal component, or part periodic in half a day, and
so on. Further terms might be added but are not usually
included : the terms here indicated give a good approximation to the observed curve. Sets of eight " harmonic "
or " Fourier " coefficients a_1, b_1, a_2, . . . b_4 are obtained
for each element at each station : since there are three
elements, each observatory supplies 24 such coefficients.
Each of these is dependent on the latitude, and 24 curves
may be plotted showing how each coefficient varies with the
latitude : because there are six curves for each of the four
periodic components (n), namely an a_n curve and a b_n
curve for each of three elements. The elements here
considered may be H, D, Z, or X, Y, Z ; the three last

are the most appropriate in the further work to be discussed.

From these 24 curves it is possible to find fairly simple mathematical expressions for each Fourier coefficient, in terms of the latitude, using for this purpose certain mathematical functions that are specially appropriate for physical quantities distributed over a sphere. This second stage in the process of mathematical representation of S_q is called spherical harmonic analysis, to which the ordinary Fourier analysis is a necessary preliminary. It is in fact found that, for the *annual mean* S_q, a single spherical harmonic function suffices to express, to a first approximation, the latitude distribution represented by each of the curves. The representation is direct in the case of Y and Z, while the differential coefficient of the function with respect to the latitude represents the X curve. But the number of different functions involved is not 24; for each periodic component n ($n = $ 1, 2, 3, 4) the six curves (an a_n curve and a b_n curve for each of three elements) are all associated with the same function (usually denoted by P_{n+1}^n); only the numerical coefficients differ from one curve to another. Thus the 24 curves are associated with only four functions P_2^1, P_3^2, P_4^3, P_5^4. Further, the a_n and b_n curves for X give approximately the same numerical factors as the two Y curves; the two Z curves give two different factors. Hence there are only sixteen numerical coefficients (eight for X and Y and eight for Z; in each case one for each a_n and one for each b_n). The expression of so many observed data by so few mathematical functions and factors is a notable fact, greatly simplifying the analysis and discussion of the material.

At the solstices (June and December), when there is summer in one hemisphere and winter in the other, the distribution of S_q is less simple, since it is not symmetrical (or antisymmetrical) with respect to the equator. At least eight harmonic functions are then required, instead of four.

The External and Internal Parts of the S_q Field.

The fact that the S_q variations in X and Y are expressible in terms of the same spherical harmonic functions—with the same numerical factors—indicates that the S_q field near the earth's surface has a potential (cf. p. 21). This implies that the field is produced by magnetism or electric currents not situated in the space near the earth's surface, where S_q is measured. Further, the difference between the pair of numerical factors associated with X and Y, and the pair associated with Z (for each periodic component) implies that the S_q field is not produced wholly below the earth's surface (as is substantially the case for the earth's main field), nor wholly above it. It is partly produced above, and partly below, and the two parts can each be determined from the four numerical factors. This analysis, the possibility of which was indicated by Gauss, was first made by Schuster. His analysis, and later analyses of the same kind, have shown that the major (" external ") part of the S_q field has its origin above the earth. The minor (" internal ") part, which has its source within the earth, contributes between a quarter and a third of the field near the earth's surface. The S_q variations due to the internal and external parts of the field reinforce one another so far as concerns the horizontal part of the S_q field, while in the vertical component they are opposed. The internal and external parts of S_q are somewhat different in *phase*, that is, in the time at which they attain their maxima ; the phase difference is nearly the same for all four periodic components. Also the ratio of the *amplitudes* of their numerical coefficients is almost the same for all the four periodic components.

Electromagnetic Induction within the Earth

In the preceding section the statements as to the separation of the S_q field into external and internal parts express facts devoid of hypothesis. It is natural, however, to consider whether or not the internal and external parts of the

S_q field, which may conveniently be denoted by S_q^i and S_q^e, are due to independent causes. The similarity of the amplitude ratios and phase differences for the four periodic components suggests a causal relation between the two parts of the field. If this is the case, we may expect the external part, S_q^e, to be the cause, and the internal part, S_q^i, to be the effect, since the former is three or four times as great (near the earth's surface) as the latter.

Actually there is an obvious way in which the S_q^e field could produce an associated internal field, namely by electromagnetic induction. A varying magnetic field surrounding the earth *must* induce electromotive forces in the body of the earth. Since the earth is to some extent an electrical conductor, these electromotive forces will impel electric earth currents. These will produce a varying magnetic field, both within and outside the earth. At and above the surface this will be reckoned as an " internal " field, proceeding from within the earth.

If we knew the electrical conductivity κ at all points throughout the earth, it would be a mere matter of calculation to determine the distribution of earth currents, and the nature of the associated internal magnetic field, induced by the known external S_q^e field. If the internal field thus calculated agreed with the S_q^i field determined directly from the magnetic observations, the latter would be completely explained. We could state as a fact, and not merely as a hypothesis, that the internal (S_q^i) field is a secondary field induced by the primary external (S_q^e) field. Actually, however, our direct knowledge of the earth's electrical conductivity does not extend beyond a depth of a few miles at most.

In these circumstances it is natural to proceed by calculating the internal field which the S_q^e field would induce in a " model " earth, of the same size as the real earth, and having some simple assumed distribution of electrical conductivity. The simplest assumption is that the conductivity κ is uniform throughout. The calculation in this case shows that, for each periodic component of the primary field, the phase difference between it and its induced field depends only on κ, and not on the size of the sphere. For fields periodic in a day, or a half, third or quarter of a day (as for S_q), the calculated phase differences are nearly equal, and their sign is the same as for the phase differences found by analysis of the actual observations of S_q. The magnitude of these observed phase differences corresponds to a value of κ, namely $3 \cdot 6 \cdot 10^{-13}$ c.g.s., which is less than the κ for sea-water ($4 \cdot 10^{-11}$), but greater than the κ for dry earth or rock (10^{-15}).

The "observed" amplitude ratios for the external and internal parts of S_q at the earth's surface, for the four periodic components, are not in agreement with those calculated for this value of κ, if it is assumed to apply throughout the whole earth. But a slightly different distribution of κ would suffice to bring calculation and observation into accord, for the amplitude ratios as well as for the phase differences : namely, a uniform distribution of κ, with the above value $3 \cdot 6 \cdot 10^{-13}$, throughout a sphere concentric with the earth, but of radius 4 per cent. less than that of the earth, the material in the outer 4 per cent. layer, of thickness about 160 miles, being non-conducting.

Thus it is possible to explain the S_q^i field as due to induction by the S_q^e field in a model earth with these simple properties, which are themselves quite reasonable from a physical standpoint. These facts seem to warrant the conclusion that the actual S_q^i field is wholly produced in this way, so that to "explain" the S_q field it remains only to seek a cause for the external part S_q^e.

It is, however, not necessary to conclude that the conductivity within the earth is zero down to 160 miles depth, and uniform in the "core" below that, with the above value. This is a possible distribution of κ consistent with the facts about S_q, but it may not be the only possible distribution consistent with these facts. Actually the oceans are more conducting than the supposed core : but they are relatively shallow, and their broken geographical distribution reduces their effectiveness as regions for the production of a secondary S_q field by induction ; it may be expected, however, that they will have sufficient influence on the internal part of the S_q field to create a difference between S_q over continents and over the oceans. The solid part of the outer 160-mile layer, which is not absolutely non-conducting, must also have some effect ; but this will be slight compared with that of the core, if κ for most of this layer has the observed value for dry earth or rock. The transition to the value $\kappa = 3 \cdot 6 \, . \, 10^{-13}$ for the core may, however, not be quite sudden, as in the " model " earth considered.

The distribution of the induced currents within the core can be calculated, and the magnetic field at the earth's surface due to the currents at any depth. It is found that the internal part of the S_q field at the surface depends mainly (i.e., to 90 per cent.) on the currents within a fifth of the depth of the core from its surface. The currents at or below a depth of half the radius of the core have no appreciable influence on the surface field. A change in the value of κ in this region could not be detected from the S_q data.

Actually there is some evidence that κ increases downwards rather rapidly between about 160 miles depth and 400 miles depth or more. For information as to κ at or below the latter depth we should need to study magnetic variations with a period much longer than one day.

The Magnetic Permeability within the Earth

The results of the calculations referred to in the preceding section are those derived on the assumption that the magnetic permeability μ within the earth is unity, i.e. that the substance of the earth is non-magnetizable. The calculations actually depend on κ/μ rather than on κ alone, so that if μ were greater than unity, the inferred value of κ would have to be increased in that ratio. There is some hope of finding, from observations of magnetic disturbance, whether μ does materially exceed unity throughout any important fraction of the earth's volume, but this has not yet been done. On physical grounds, however, it seems unlikely that μ does much exceed unity. A larger value would presumably imply the existence of ferromagnetic material within the core. But at ordinary pressures iron loses its magnetizability at 860° C., a temperature attained at about 60 miles depth ; and increased pressure appears only to lower the temperature at which iron ceases to be magnetizable (cf. p. 26).

THE EXTERNAL PART OF THE S_q FIELD, S_q^e

The problem of the origin of the S_q field is now reduced to that of its external part S_q^e. This is directly known only at the surface, but its value can be calculated at any height up to which there is no magnetic matter and no electric current. The air is practically non-magnetic and non-conducting up to about 90 km. height, above which there are two main ionized layers, one (the E layer) at about 100 km. and the other (the F layer) at 200 or 250 km. height, with subsidiary layers in between. These are ionized daily by the sun, and their ion-content decreases at night. The order of magnitude of the maximum electron content per c.c. in the E layer is 10^5, and in the F layer about five times as great. The electron-content above the F layer is unknown, but is less than in the F layer.

Since there is no magnetic matter (in the ordinary sense) above the earth's surface, the S_q^e field must be produced in some ionized region. This is likely to be situated in our atmosphere, and to be ionized daily by the sun, as are the E and F layers : because this is consonant with the observed distribution of the S_q field, which is more intense over the sunlit than over the dark hemisphere, while there is little likelihood that an ionized region so distributed exists or could maintain itself outside the earth's atmosphere. Now the atmosphere is relatively thin, compared with the radius of the earth. Hence the S_q^e field may be said to originate in a thin spherical layer of atmosphere, concentric with the earth.

The spherical harmonic analysis of the S_q field, and the resulting expression for the external part S_q^e, fortunately affords a means of calculating the strength and direction of the system of currents, flowing in such a thin spherical layer, that could produce the S_q^e field ; or, alternatively, it indicates what distribution of magnetization in such a shell could produce the field. Such a current system, or such a distribution of magnetization, may be solely responsible for the S_q^e field, or the two causes may be jointly responsible ; no other alternative seems possible.

THE S_q^e ATMOSPHERIC SYSTEM OF ELECTRIC CURRENTS

Figs. 14, 15 illustrate the distribution of the atmospheric system of electric currents which could produce the S_q^e field. They are drawn on a Mercator projection, but their meridians of longitude are not fixed relative to the earth, but rotate with the sun : that is, the distributions appear always the same as viewed from the sun, except for the slow seasonal changes (cf. p. 38). Fig. 14 refers to the equinoctial periods, and Fig. 15 to June, the season of northern summer and southern winter. The closed curves show the direction of current flow, and are drawn at such distances apart that 10,000 amperes flow between each pair of adjacent current lines. The currents flow in four main circuits, two north and two south of the equator at the equinoxes, though at the solstices the circuits in the summer hemisphere (the northern one in Fig. 15) are intensified relative to those in the winter hemisphere, and extend across the equator into this hemisphere. The two circuits on either side of the equator are approximately situated one over the sunlit and one over the night hemisphere, and the former is much the more intense ; the total current-flow in the day-circuit is 62,000 amperes at the equinoxes, rising to 89,000 amperes in summer.

It may be that additional electric currents flow round the earth along the parallels of latitude ; such currents would contribute to the general field of the earth, without affecting S_q^e ; and they would modify the current lines in Figs 14, 15.

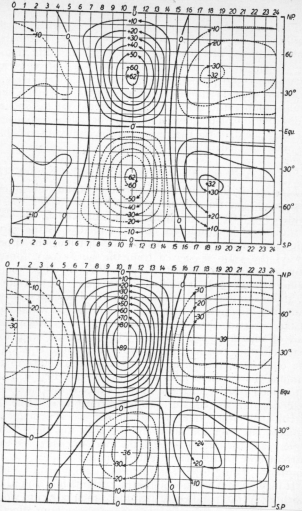

FIGS. 14 and 15.—Atmospheric systems of electric currents which could produce the solar daily magnetic variation.

Above : at the equinoxes.   Below : in June.

Possible Causes of an S_q^e Electric Current System

It is not known whether the S_q^e field is due to a system of electric currents in the upper atmosphere. Let us for the sake of discussion suppose that it is. The magnetic data give no indication of the height above the earth at which the currents will be situated: that has to be found from independent data, such as are afforded by the radio exploration of the atmosphere. From the knowledge thus gained it seems that the E or the F layer, or both, are the most likely regions for the currents. The physical conditions in these layers are very different, apart from the stronger ionization in the F layer; the air is much rarer, and possibly hotter, in the F than in the E layer.

If we knew how the ionization varied in the E and F layers over a period of many years, it might be possible to find out in which of them S_q^e is produced, by noting a correspondence between the variations of the general intensity of S_q and the changes of ionization in one or other layer; but the radio data concerning the upper atmosphere do not extend far enough back to permit this. At present the level of the origin of the S_q^e field remains in doubt.

Two possible causes of a current system of the type shown in Figs. 14, 15 have been suggested. According to one theory, generally known as the *dynamo theory*, the currents are induced by a convective motion of the atmosphere across the earth's permanent magnetic field; diurnal and semi-diurnal motions of the atmosphere occur at ground level, and motions of the same type in the E or F layer would induce therein a system of currents of the right type. We cannot be sure that the motion of the atmosphere at those heights is the same as near the ground, but if we assume that it is, the necessary electric conductivity of the current layer can be calculated; in order of magnitude it is similar to, though perhaps somewhat in excess of, the probable total conductivity of the E layer, which itself probably exceeds that of the F layer (where, owing to the rarity of the atmosphere at these levels, and the presence of the magnetic field, the electric conductivity across the direction of the magnetic field is much less than along the field). The data necessary to test the dynamo theory are really not at present available, both because of our ignorance of the high-level convective motion, and because the conductivity depends on the density of the atmosphere there, which is still uncertain.

A theory known as the *drift-current theory* offers an alternative explanation of the currents. In rarefied levels, where the electrons and ions are free to spiral round the earth's lines of magnetic force, the weight of these particles causes them to execute a trochoidal motion with a general drift to eastward for the positive ions and to westward for the electrons: the two motions combine to give an eastward electric " drift " current. If the ionization were the same all along each circle of latitude, the currents would likewise be uniform along each circle, and would not produce any daily variation of the field; but the actual day-to-night inequality of ionization would require the currents to diverge from the parallels of latitude, and it is suggested (though the theory has not been worked out in any detail, as the dynamo theory has), that their resulting distribution would be of the right type and of the right order of magnitude. Until this theory has been more fully developed its merits or demerits cannot be properly assessed. For the present, the origin of the S_q^e current-system (if a current-system *is* the cause of S_q^e) must remain in doubt, but the exceptionally large S_q variations found at Huancayo, Peru, favour the dynamo theory.

THE DIAMAGNETIC THEORY OF THE S_q^e FIELD

Another theory of the origin of the S_q^e field, which was actually second in order of date of proposal, is that the field is due to diamagnetism of the ionized layers. The spiral motion of the electrons and ions in the E and F layers, which are not in thermodynamic equilibrium, must render these layers diamagnetic. The distribution of diamagnetism is approximately of the right type to produce a field qualitatively similar to the S_q field. The intensity of the diamagnetism depends on the number of electrons and ions present, and on their (random) speeds, which will depend on the temperature of the ionized layer. The temperature in the E and F layers is not known, and unless it is very high (e.g. above 1000° C.) the diamagnetism may be inadequate to account for the S_q^e field.

THE YEAR-TO-YEAR VARIATION OF IONIZATION

Leaving in suspense the decision as to the origin of the S_q^e field, one point common to all three theories of the field may be noted : the intensity of the field is governed by the degree of ionization in the " S_q " layer where the field is produced. Hence this ionization must, like S_q^e, be considerably greater in years of sunspot maximum than of sunspot minimum. This betokens a variation of the solar ionizing agent which far exceeds any solar-cycle variation in the radiation received at ground level. As the solar ionizing agent is, at least in part, ultraviolet light, it thus appears that this end of the solar spectrum varies much more with the sunspot epoch than does the longer-wave radiation which is able to penetrate through the whole atmosphere of the earth. It is probable that neutral solar corpuscles also play a part in the ionization of the upper atmosphere.

THE EFFECT OF A SOLAR ECLIPSE UPON S_q AND UPON THE IONIZED LAYERS

It has been found by radio measurements that during a total eclipse of the sun the ionization of the upper air in the eclipsed region decreases by about one-half. This must affect the current-system or the diamagnetism to which S_q is due. Attempts have been made to observe the change in S_q which must thus result, but it has not yet proved possible to detect them with certainty.

The observed decrease in the ionization of the E and F layers during a solar eclipse occurs over the eclipsed region, at the time of the eclipse, whereas if the ionization were due to neutral corpuscles from the sun, travelling with a speed much less than that of light, the decrease of ionization should occur earlier, and to the east of the darkened eclipse region. Thus it is proved that the E and F layers are ionized mainly by ultraviolet light (or by corpuscles travelling with practically the same speed). Possibly further observations may reveal the presence of other layers ionized by neutral corpuscles.

CHAPTER IV

THE LUNAR DAILY MAGNETIC VARIATION L

THE COMPUTATION OF L

THE solar daily magnetic variation S may be removed from the hourly magnetic data for each element by subtracting, from each hourly value during (say) a month, the mean departure for the month, at that solar hour, from the monthly mean. The revised hourly values thus obtained will vary because of magnetic disturbance and also because of L. Suppose that these hourly values are rearranged in rows each containing 24 or 25 successive values, the initial value in each row being for an hour nearest to that of lunar transit. On taking the means of the columns, it may be assumed (provided the number of rows, each corresponding to one lunar day, is sufficiently great) that the variations due to magnetic disturbance will average out, not being related to lunar time. The series of hourly means will thus give the mean lunar daily magnetic variation, or, if the mean of all is subtracted from each, the lunar daily magnetic inequality for the element. Since the disturbance variations, and also S, are so much greater than L, and since S is not constant from day to day, many precautions have to be observed in finding L, and material from many years is necessary if reliable results are to be obtained. But when found, it can be discussed and represented graphically just like S itself.

THE MONTHLY MEAN L IS SEMI-DIURNAL

L can be determined from all days over a given period, such as a year, or all days in a group of months, such as all Januaries for a number of years. When so determined, it is found to be of notably simple character; its graph, whatever the element or station, is a double sine wave; that is to say, L is semi-diurnal. For different stations and elements L differs, of course, in amplitude and phase (that is, in the range between the two equal maxima and two equal minima, and in the times—separated by a quarter of the lunar day—at which these maxima and minima occur). When the curves for the separate elements are combined to form the vector diagram, they give an oval curve which is described twice daily: the central curve in Fig. 16 shows such a vector diagram for the horizontal plane.

L at the Separate Lunar Phases

It is possible, however, to determine L from a number of days all (within narrow limits) at the same phase or age of the moon; e.g. new moon, half moon, or full moon. Any such phase or age corresponds to a definite angle between the lines drawn to the sun and the moon from the centre of the Earth; it corresponds also to a definite difference between the hours of solar and lunar time, so that the hours of daylight (or of darkness) will fall in a particular section of the lunar day, at a particular age of the moon. At new moon, for instance, the sun and moon are on the same meridian, and noon, about which the hours of daylight are centred, is also the middle of the lunar day; at full moon, on the other hand, the hours of *darkness* are in the middle of the lunar day, and so on. Thus, if the graph representing L (for any element and station) is thickened during the part of the lunar day corresponding to daylight, different parts of the graph will be thickened at different ages of the moon. It is found that when the graph of L, determined from days all at a particular lunar phase, is drawn in this way, the thickened daylight part of the graph has a greater range than the remaining (night) portion; L is no longer semi-diurnal. Moreover, the series of these graphs, drawn for successive ages of the

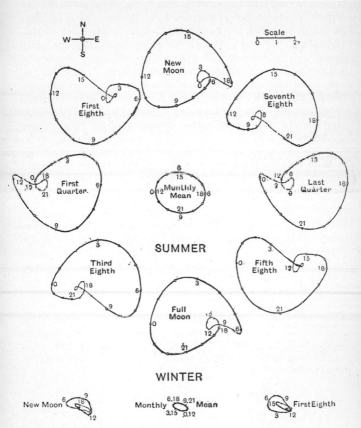

Fig. 16.—Vector diagrams for the lunar daily variation of horizontal magnetic force at Pavlovsk, in summer (above) and winter (below): for the mean of a number of whole lunations (in the centre), and also at various particular epochs in the lunation.

moon, appears to be such as might be obtained from the simple double-wave graph for L as derived from all days of the months, by increasing the range of this curve during the hours of sunlight and reducing it during the dark hours. In the course of a lunar month, or a number of lunar months, each lunar hour occurs equally often at all epochs of sunlight and darkness, and this light-to-darkness inequality of the curves is averaged out to give a simple double wave. But the L curves at particular lunar ages show that L, like S, is more active during sunlight than during darkness.

THE VECTOR DIAGRAMS FOR L AT THE SEPARATE LUNAR PHASES

As a consequence, the vector diagram for L at any time is not really a twice-repeated oval, but a combination of two loops; the part of the figure (not necessarily a complete loop) that corresponds to the sunlight hours is much larger than the remaining night portion. This is shown in Fig. 16; the upper part of this figure gives, in the centre, the horizontal force vector diagram for L as determined at Pavlovsk from a number of (whole) summer months; this diagram is an ellipse, described twice daily. Round this ellipse are disposed the vector diagrams obtained at eight epochs in the lunar month, from new moon, through full moon, back to new moon again. The amplification of the loop in the changing sunlit portion of the lunar day is clearly shown.

THE ANNUAL VARIATION OF L

The lower part of Fig. 16 gives the corresponding winter diagrams for the monthly mean L, and for L at two lunar phases. It shows how very much smaller L is in winter than in summer at this station, at latitude 60° N. On comparison with Fig. 12, p. 46, for S_q at Greenwich, in a latitude only slightly lower, it illustrates the fact (amply confirmed by examination of the data for other stations) that the annual variation of L is decidedly greater than that of S_q. This fact is exemplified in a manner that is more comprehensive, and therefore perhaps still more convincing, in the current-system diagrams (Figs. 18, 19) referred to on page 71.

THE RELATION OF L TO THE SUNSPOT CYCLE

Since L is closely connected with the sun, as shown by the greater activity of L during the hours of sunlight than

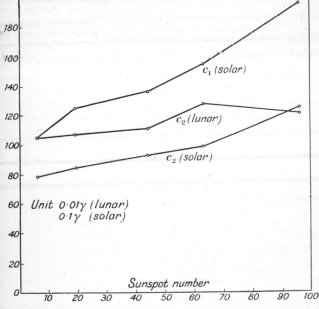

FIG. 17.—The dependence on solar spottedness of certain harmonic components of the daily magnetic variations, solar and lunar.

during the night (Fig. 16), and also by its large annual variation, it is natural to expect that L will, like S_q, show a change from year to year in approximate correspondence with the eleven-year sunspot cycle. However, this expectation is surprisingly at variance with the facts. It is not easy to illustrate this by means of a diagram for L corresponding to Fig. 13 (p. 48), for the reason that one year is not long enough to yield a reliable determination of L. It is therefore necessary to determine L for *groups* of years, classified according to their mean sunspot number; it is convenient also, for comparison, to determine the mean S_q for the same groups of years. A diagram on which the range (or some other index of the magnitude) of S_q and of L is plotted against the mean sunspot number then shows that though S_q increases nearly twofold from the group of least to that of greatest mean sunspot number, L shows only a very slight increase. Fig. 17 is such a diagram, constructed for S_q and L for Greenwich magnetic declination, and based on no less than 63 years' hourly data for this element. The index used to represent the magnitude of L is the semi-range C_2 of the annual mean L, which is purely semi-diurnal; for S_q two indices are used, one being the semi-range C_2 of the semi-diurnal component of S_q (which is $\sqrt{(a_2^2 + b_2^2)}$—cf. page 50), and the other the semi-range C_1 of the diurnal component. The scale for C_2 (lunar) is ten times more open than that for the solar C_1 and C_2.

Day-to-Day Variations of L on Quiet Days

It would be highly interesting to know whether L, like S_q, undergoes day-to-day variations of range on quiet days; but there seems little hope of finding whether or not this is so, because it is impossible to determine L for a single day; it may be possible, however, to determine L for groups of quiet days on which the range of S_q is greater or less than the normal, and thus to determine whether the range of L follows, on the average, the same course as that of S_q.

THE VARIATION OF L WITH THE MAGNETIC ACTIVITY

The solar daily variation consists of a part, S_q, which is seen in its pure form on quiet days, and persists also throughout disturbed periods, but is then combined with another part, S_D, which is constant in form but varies in intensity, in parallel with the general degree of disturbance. It is of interest to examine whether or not L is the same on disturbed as on quiet days, by determining L separately from groups of days classified according to their magnetic activity.

It is thus found that L increases in amplitude, apparently without any great change of form at individual stations, as the disturbance increases. The increase of L varies very much with the element and the locality. For the declination at Batavia, south of the magnetic equator, L varies nearly ten-fold in summer from the sixty quietest to the sixty most disturbed days per year ; for the declination at Greenwich the variation is much less, only two-fold (though this is of course a considerable change) ; the variations for other elements and stations lie between these limits. There is need for further work on this important relation between L and magnetic disturbance, which seems destined to throw much light on the physical cause of L.

THE MATHEMATICAL REPRESENTATION OF L

The processes of harmonic and spherical harmonic analyses can be applied to L just as to S (cf. p. 50). It is found that the semi-diurnal component of L is constant in phase throughout the month, while the phases of the other components undergo a regular monthly variation ; the phase of the first component ($n = 1$) decreases through a complete cycle (2π) from one new moon to the next, while that of the third component increases by the same amount. The phase of the fourth component increases by twice this amount (4π) per month. These variations of phase correspond to the change of form of L, by which at each epoch in the lunar month the variation during the sunlit hours is intensified.

The spherical harmonic representation of L, say at new moon, is very similar to that of S_q. The main functions involved (four at the equinoxes and at least eight at the solstices) are the same; the numerical coefficients are smaller for L than for S_q, and bear somewhat different

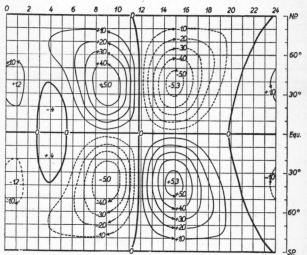

Fig. 18.—Atmospheric systems of electric currents which could produce the lunar daily magnetic variation: at the equinoxes (Fig. 18), and in June (Fig. 19.)

relations to one another. In particular, the four extra harmonic functions required at the solstices to represent the seasonal difference then existing between the two hemispheres have relatively larger coefficients for L than for S_q; this corresponds to the greater annual variation of L than of S_q, already noted (p. 66).

The numerical factors of the harmonic functions determined from X and Y on the one hand and from Z on the other enable the internal and external parts (L^i, L^e) of the L field to be determined, as for S_q. The amplitude ratios and phase differences between the inner and outer parts of each harmonic term in the potential of L are closely similar to those for the corresponding terms in the potential of S_q. Since the periods in the two cases are nearly the same, it follows that the internal part of the L field (L^i) can be explained as due to currents induced in the earth

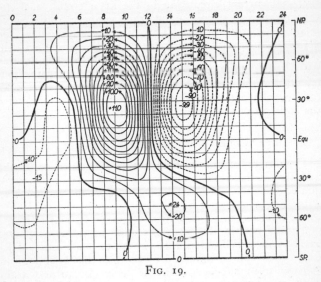

Fig. 19.

by the varying outer L field (L^e), with the same inferred distribution of electrical conductivity within the earth as was found from S_q (p. 52).

THE CURRENT-DIAGRAMS FOR L

The spherical harmonic expression for the potential of the outer L field enables a hypothetical current-diagram to be drawn, showing the overhead current-system in the atmosphere which could produce the L^e field. It is shown in Figs. 18, 19, for the period of new moon; Fig. 18 refers to the equinoxes, and Fig. 19 to the June solstice. The meridians refer to local lunar time; at new moon the sun and the moon are both on the 12^h meridian. The current lines are drawn at intervals of 1000 amperes. Comparison with Figs. 14, 15 shows that the current-system for L is weaker than that for S_q in the ratio about 1 to 12, the total current circulating in the main circuit of L (at the equinoxes) being about 5300 amperes, as against 62,000 amperes for S_q. The diagrams well show the greater intensity of the currents over the sunlit than over the dark hemisphere. Fig. 19 shows in a striking way how great is the seasonal variation of L, the summer sunlit circuit (in the northern hemisphere in June) carrying a total current of 11,000 amperes, which is more than twice the strength of the equinoctial circuit.

THE ORIGIN OF THE L FIELD

The origin of the L field seems less open to doubt than that of the S_q field, because the moon is so much more limited than the sun in its ability to affect the earth. The semi-diurnal character of the L field, when averaged over whole months, suggests a tidal origin of L, and it seems practically certain that the lunar tide in the atmosphere, which is now well-determined, is the primary cause of L. This conclusion is supported by the fact that L appears to increase from apogee (when the moon is furthest from the earth) to perigee (when it is nearest) in approximately the same ratio as the moon's tide-producing force, that is, inversely as the cube of the moon's distance: though the proof of this relation for L is not yet so decisive as could be desired, owing to special difficulties in the computation of L from groups of days selected according to the moon's distance.

Of the three hypotheses as to the origin of S_q, described on pp. 59-61, only one is applicable to L, namely, the dynamo theory.   Calculation shows that the horizontal air currents associated with a lunar atmospheric tide would induce electric currents having an L field of the same type as the *semi-diurnal component* of the observed L^e field, if the electrical conductivity of the atmospheric layer in which the electric currents flow were uniform ;   if, however, as in the actual atmosphere, the ionization and conductivity are greater over the sunlit hemisphere than over the dark hemisphere, the other periodic components of L are produced, with amplitudes and changing phases, as observed. Thus qualitatively, and to a large extent also quantitatively, the tidal-dynamo hypothesis well explains L ;   but there remain two uncertainties, concerning the actual magnitude and phase of L, and the height of the " L-layer " wherein L is produced.   The phase of L differs from that which would result if the phase of the tide in the " L-layer " were the same as that of the tide observed at the ground ;   it seems necessary to conclude that in the L layer the tide has a very different phase.   The theory of the tide itself does not suffice at present to predict or explain such a change of phase with height.   If, however, the phase is different from that near the ground, the amplitude of the tide may also be unexpectedly different.   If it were known, we could deduce the conductivity of the L layer from the observed magnitude of L, but our uncertainty as to the amplitude of the tide precludes this calculation.

The height of the L-layer is unknown.   The magnetic data do not suffice to determine it, and the identification of the L-layer with any of the ionized layers observed by radio methods must await a satisfactory correlation between the changes of ionization of one of these layers and the changes of magnitude of L.   The difference between the changes of L and those of S_q, throughout the sunspot cycle, seems to imply that S_q and L are produced in different layers.   The large dependence of the magnitude of L on the degree of magnetic activity suggests that L is produced in a layer ionized by neutral corpuscles from the sun (cf. p. 61).

CHAPTER V

THE MORPHOLOGY OF THE MAGNETIC DISTURBANCE FIELD D

MAGNETIC DISTURBANCE AND STORMS

MAGNETIC disturbance may be regarded as due to the superposition, upon the normal magnetic field existing during quiet periods, of an additional disturbance or D field (p. 39). The study of the changing " form " of this field, that is, of its changing geographical distribution, may be called the morphology of the D field. This forms the subject of the present chapter. In Chapter VI other important aspects of magnetic disturbance are considered, relating to the incidence of disturbance in *time*.

By examining sets of magnetographs drawn from observatories widely distributed over the earth, it is found that the intensity of disturbance increases from low to high latitudes, up to magnetic latitude (about) 67°, which is the latitude of the zones of most frequent occurrence of auroræ (or, briefly, of *the auroral zones*) ; within these zones the intensity somewhat decreases towards the poles of the earth's magnetic axis, but nevertheless is still considerable. On this account the magnetic traces are seldom quite undisturbed in high latitudes, for there a tenth (say) of the disturbance existing on average days is quite perceptible, while in the tropics it is insignificant.

The intensity of disturbance varies greatly with the time ; disturbance of low intensity may be confined to a small part of the earth's surface, but intense disturbance is a world-wide phenomenon, affecting both northern and southern hemispheres simultaneously. Such intense world-wide magnetic disturbances are called *magnetic storms*. A striking feature of the most outstanding magnetic storms is that they usually commence suddenly, at almost the same instant all over the earth; the differences between the times of their onset at different stations seem to be of the order of half a minute. In less intense storms the commencement is not so abrupt, but it can often be defined to within an hour.

Magnetic disturbance seems infinitely various in its details, but there is nevertheless much regularity about its average features. The following is one way in which this is brought to light.

The Storm-Time Variations

A number of magnetic storms are chosen, of roughly similar intensity, and with their times of commencement (not necessarily sudden, but known within one hour) distributed fairly evenly over the twenty-four hours of the Greenwich day. Successive hourly values of a chosen magnetic element at a chosen station are written out in rows of 24 or 48 or more, commencing in each row with the value for the hour preceding the storm. The columns are added and the means taken, giving a row of 24 or more mean hourly values of the element, for the first day or more, averaged over all the storms. In this average, any changes, such as S_q and S_D (p. 34), which depend on the time of day or solar hour-angle, will cancel out, because each hour of the day, with its appropriate S_q or S_D departure from the means, will occur roughly the same number of times in each column, owing to the nearly uniform distribution of the hours of commencement over all hours of the day. Thus the changes indicated by the final row of means will represent that part of the disturbance changes which depends on time reckoned from the commencement of the storm ; this may conveniently be called *storm-time*.

To obtain a general view of these storm-time changes it is necessary to determine them for each element from a number of observatories. Fig. 20 shows the results thus obtained from the records at 11 observatories, for a set of 40 storms of moderate intensity. It gives the average storm-time changes during the first two days of these storms. The three sections of the diagram, left, middle, and right, refer to groups of stations in different magnetic latitudes.

The storm-time changes in horizontal (approximately north) force clearly much exceed those in the other two elements : the horizontal force is first increased, and remains above the initial undisturbed value for a period of two to four hours. This may be called the *initial phase* of the storm. But after quickly attaining a maximum, H decreases, and after several hours attains a minimum ; this minimum is much more below the initial undisturbed value than the maximum is above it. From this minimum there is a slow recovery towards the normal value : the rate of recovery at first increases, but soon becomes increasingly slow, and is clearly incomplete at the end of two days. The recovery continues indeed over many days, some of which may be quite free from any sign of disturbance other than this residual effect. The period during which H is below the normal value, up to the time when the rate of recovery ceases to increase, may be called the *main phase* of the storm, and the subsequent period may be called the *last phase*, or *phase of recovery*.

It is thus clear that a magnetic storm must depress the mean value of the horizontal force for the month in which it occurs ; and since on disturbed days there is on the average a decrease in H, on quiet days there must on the average be a slight compensating increase during the day. Hence the value of H for the initial midnight for a quiet day will in the average be less than that of the closing midnight. This is called the *aperiodic* or *non-cyclic* change of H on quiet days.

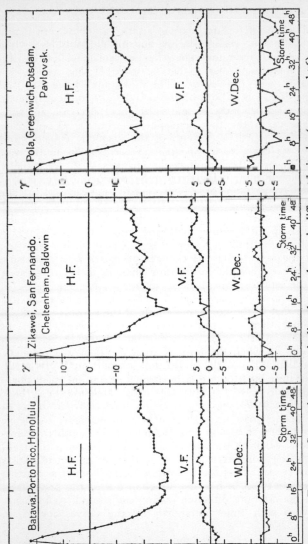

Fig. 20.—Storm-time magnetic disturbance changes in different latitudes (pp. 41 and 76).

The magnetic declination seems to show practically no storm-time change (in low and middle latitudes), while the vertical force undergoes changes much smaller than H, and opposite in sign ; that is, when H decreases V increases, and *vice versa*. The horizontal force has the same direction in both northern and southern hemispheres, and its initial increase and subsequent decrease are simultaneous in the two hemispheres. But V has opposite directions north and south of the magnetic equator, and since its changes in *magnitude* (V) are similar in the two hemispheres, the simultaneous changes in Z are actually opposite in sign. Hence it is to be expected that the storm-time change in V or Z will vanish (or nearly so) at the magnetic equator.

These storm-time changes in H and V follow a similar course in all latitudes over the range, up to about 55° magnetic latitude (N. or S.), represented in Fig. 20 ; but the range of the H changes decreases with increasing latitude. Thus the storm-time changes in H are greatest at the equator, where those in V vanish. The range of the storm-time changes in V seems likely to have maxima somewhat to the north and south of the equator.

Since there is (practically) no storm-time change of declination, the storm-time portion of the D field must be one in which the lines of force lie along the magnetic meridians. Since the storm-time changes in V are small, these lines must be *nearly* horizontal during the main phase of the storm ; that is, they are nearly parallel to the surface, though *actually* they approach the surface from above, at a slight inclination, in the northern hemisphere, and leave the surface at a slight inclination in the southern hemisphere. During the first phase their direction is reversed. Thus the storm-time field, over this range of latitude, is of very simple form ; symmetrical about the earth's (magnetic) axis, it has one direction during the first phase, and the opposite direction during the second, its intensity varying with time, as shown by the curves for H in Fig. 20.

The Disturbance Daily Variation S_D

The actual variations of H, declination and V in any individual storm will, of course, differ materially from the average storm-time curves of Fig. 20, because they also include S_q, S_D and the irregular variations D_i peculiar to the storm. It is of interest to examine these variations after subtracting from them the average storm-time changes. Thus, taking one of the sheets of hourly values used, as described on p. 75, to determine the storm-time changes, we subtract the average values written at the foot of the sheet from all the hourly values in the corresponding columns above. The hourly differences thus formed, for the first day of each storm (and likewise for the second day) may then be re-written on further (" local-time ") sheets, in columns each corresponding to the appropriate hour of local time, 1, 2, 3 . . . 24; e.g., in the case of a storm commencing, say, at 17^h local time, which for this storm is counted as 0^h storm-time, the first eight hourly differences from the storm-time sheets refer to local times 17 to 24, and the next 16 hourly differences refer to local times 1 to 16 ; hence, on the local-time sheets of hourly differences for the first day of the storm the first eight hourly differences from the storm-time sheets are written *after* the next sixteen. On forming the average value for each column, on the local-time sheets, the mean solar daily variation of the element is obtained for the first day of this group of storms, at the station considered. Inspection shows that while this differs considerably from S_q, it seems to include S_q together with a variation of quite different type, which of course is S_D. The latter is found by subtracting S_q from this total mean daily variation for the first day of the storm.

Figs. 21-23 give for each element, H, declination, and V, curves showing S_q in the left-hand section, S_D for the first day of the storm in the middle section, and S_D for the second day of the storm in the right-hand section. In each section curves are given for stations, or groups of stations, in different magnetic latitudes, as follows :

(1) Sitka (mag. lat. 60°).
(2) Pavlovsk (mag. lat. 56°).
(3) Mean of Pola, Potsdam, Greenwich (mag. lat. 51°).

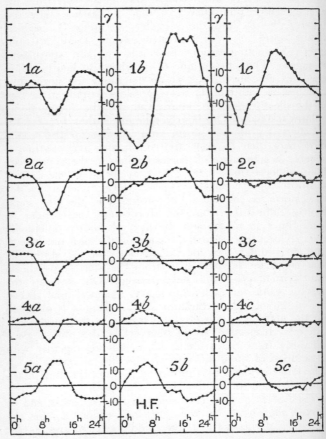

FIG. 21.—Quiet and disturbance daily variations in H (p. 79).

(4) Mean of Zikawei, San Fernando, Cheltenham, Baldwin (40°).
(5) Mean of Batavia, Porto Rico, Honolulu (22°).

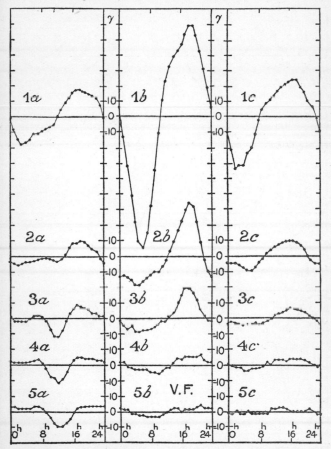

FIG. 22.—Quiet and disturbance daily variations in V (p. 79).

6

The S_D curves relate to the same storms as those on which Fig. 20 is based. Those for the second day are similar to those for the first, but of smaller amplitude. The S_D

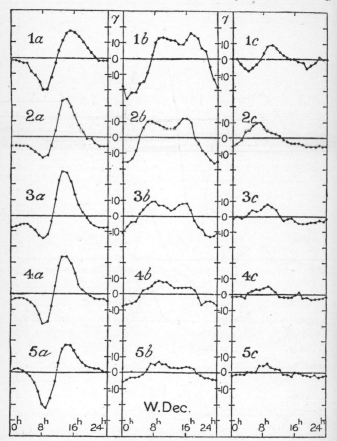

FIG. 23.—Quiet and disturbance daily variations in W. Dec. (p. 79).

curves are obviously very different from the S_q curves, both in the times of their maximum, minimum and zero values and in their relation to the latitude. Particularly notable is the increase of S_D in H, and still more in V, from Pavlovsk to Sitka. Unlike the S_q curves, the S_D curves show no greater intensity of change during the sunlit hours than during the dark hours.

The S_D curves represent a variation due to a part of the D field which we may call the S_D field : it depends on local time, and so may be thought of as constant in form and position (though not in intensity) as viewed from the sun (pp. 36-39); the S_D changes at any station are thus regarded as the result of the passage of the station along a path through the S_D field, consequent on the earth's daily rotation. The S_D field is not of constant intensity, but decreases from the first to the second day of a storm. This suggests, though it is insufficient to prove, that although the S_D field has a definite form, its intensity varies in rough accordance with that of the storm-time field. Whether the S_D field is actually reversed during the first phase of a storm, like the storm-time field, has not yet been ascertained. But apart from this first phase, the general picture which this discussion suggests is that the whole D field consists of the combination of the storm-time (D_{st}) and S_D fields, varying similarly in intensity with time, together with a more local and fluctuating field D_i, corresponding to the irregular features of the individual storm.

THE RELATION OF FORM TO INTENSITY OF THE D FIELD

Since the *intensity* of magnetic disturbance varies over a wide range, it is of importance to know how far the *form* of the D field varies with the intensity. Groups of " great " and " very great " storms, respectively twice and four times as intense as those to which Fig. 20 refers, were therefore examined, for two stations, Bombay and Pavlovsk, one in low and one in high latitude. The storm-time variation in H, and also S_D for the first two days of the storms, were determined and are represented in Fig. 24; the scales used for the curves for the great and very great storms are only $\frac{1}{2}$ and $\frac{1}{4}$ those for the moderate storms already discussed. The three sets of curves are thus reduced to similar dimensions, and are clearly of similar form : though there is one significant difference, that H appears to attain its minimum phase earlier for the very great than for the more moderate storms. The S_q curves are fairly similar for the three sets of storms. Fig. 24 thus supports the view that the regular (storm-time and S_D) part of the D field is substantially the same in form and in its time-changes, over a four-fold range of intensity.

It is desirable to know whether the approximate constancy of type of the D field still holds for magnetic disturbance much less intense than the moderate storms of Figs. 20-24. But this cannot be tested in the same detailed way, because such disturbance is usually not marked by any sudden commencement, so that the time corresponding to storm-time cannot be identified. It is indeed difficult to discern whether a prolonged period of minor disturbance is made up of one or of many individual disturbances. This difficulty has prevented the determination of the course of the storm-time changes for weak disturbance. Nevertheless a partial test of their similarity with those for strong disturbance can be made, as follows :—

The Disturbance-Change in the Daily Mean Field, D_m

The local-time changes considered in Figs. 21-23 are measured from the daily mean value of the magnetic element as origin, and so are independent of the absolute value of this mean. The storm-time changes, on the other hand, directly affect the daily mean value, and the way in which they will do so on ordinary days of slight disturbance, if they remain of the same type as in magnetic storms, can be inferred on the reasonable assumption that, when a large number of more or less disturbed days

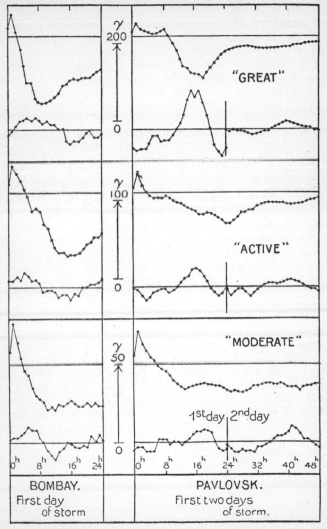

FIG. 24.—Storm-time and disturbance daily variations for storms of different intensities (p. 83).

is considered, each hour of the day will experience approximately the same average storm-time effect. For example, during the first few hours of a magnetic storm the horizontal force is generally increased (taking the average round a parallel of latitude so as to allow for S_D), but subsequently it experiences a much larger and more prolonged decrease, which dies away slowly ; thus the average storm-time effect on the horizontal force should be a decrease in the daily mean during disturbance. The magnitude of the decrease should hava a maximum at the equator, and should diminish with increasing latitude, to about half the equatorial value in latitude 50° or 55°. The vertical force storm-time changes are much smaller than those in H, and opposite in sign, but otherwise they follow a similar course. The average effect on the daily mean of the downward vertical force should be a very slight increase, in moderate northern latitudes : the effect should vanish at the equator, and be reversed (like the whole vertical force) in the southern hemisphere. The declination shows no appreciable storm-time changes in lower and middle latitudes, and hence its daily mean value should not be affected by disturbance.

These expectations, based on the supposition that the storm-time changes are similar in type for strong and weak disturbance, are well confirmed by the observed data, as the following Table shows. It gives the differences obtained by subtracting the daily mean values of the three magnetic elements, for *quiet* days, from the corresponding daily means for *all* days. The magnetic latitudes of the stations dealt with are indicated in brackets.

		H.F.	V.F.	W.Dec
(1)	Sitka (60°)	− 3	− 3	o
(2)	Pavlovsk (56°)	− 5	o	o
(3)	Greenwich (54°)	− 4	o	o
(4)	Cheltenham (50°)	− 7	1	o
(5)	Honolulu (21°)	− 10	1	1

The results are given to the nearest unit (1γ), and are probably accurate to within about 1γ. Though they do not all refer to the same series of years, a different choice would not alter the general indications of the Table. The changes observed are small except in the case of H, where they are systematic, and in good agreement with expectation. This extends the evidence for the substantial constancy of type of the D field to intensities much lower than those of Fig. 20; but this extension of the proof, which relates to the storm-time changes only, is only partial, because it deals only with the daily-average of the storm-time changes ; this is what was called D_m in Chapter II.

THE RELATION OF FORM TO INTENSITY OF S_D

A more complete proof can be given for the constancy of type of the S_D part of the D field, down to low orders of magnetic disturbance. The evidence is contained in Figs. 9-11, p. 42, which are analogous to Figs. 21-23. In both sets of figures the first column (a) gives the whole average daily variation on quiet days, that is, on the five quiet days per month chosen internationally ; the curves (b) show the daily variations, *additional* to those in section (a), which are observed on the first days of magnetic storms. But whereas in Figs. 21-23 the curves (c) refer to the second days of magnetic storms, in Figs. 9-11 the curves (c) show the daily variations (likewise *additional* to those in section (a)) observed on ordinary or average (i.e. the mean of all) days. These curves thus represent the hourly differences between the average daily variations on all days and on quiet days, and show the S_D variations corresponding to the slight degree of disturbance present on the average day. The curves (c) in Figs. 9-11 relate to the stations mentioned in the Table above.

Thus the curves (b) and (c) in Figs. 9-11 represent S_D on (b) moderately strong and (c) relatively weak magnetic disturbance. In spite of various minor irregularities, many of which would disappear if averages from a larger amount of material had been taken, the 15 independent curves (b) show a considerable degree of similarity with the corresponding 15 curves (c), while the curves

(b) and (c) are obviously quite different from the curves (a).* For example, in Fig. 9 there is a reversal of type in section (a) in a low latitude (about 30°, between curves 4 and 5), whereas in sections (b) and (c), though there is also a reversal of type, it occurs in a much higher latitude (about 55°, between curves 2 and 3). Moreover, in Fig. 9, section (a), the extreme departures from the mean occur in the middle of the day, at about the time when curves (b) and (c) cross the zero line. The latter contrast is shown also by Fig. 10, though in other respects this differs greatly from Fig. 9. In Fig. 11 the curves (a) cross the zero line at about mid-day, while the curves (b) and (c) cross it at about 6^h and 18^h. These three Figs., which summarize a great mass of evidence, agree with Fig. 24 and the results of the above Table in indicating that the D field is approximately constant in type, over a great range of intensity of disturbance.

DISTURBANCE IN HIGH LATITUDES

So far the morphology of magnetic disturbance has been discussed for the belt of the earth lying between (magnetic) latitudes $\pm$ 60°. The regions of higher latitude, forming the polar caps, remain to be considered : they are found to be of special interest. There the disturbance field is most intense, most variable in time, and most complex in geographical distribution. Owing to the severe climate the social and economic circumstances there are unfavourable to the establishment and maintenance of magnetic observatories. Hence until fairly recent years there were no permanent magnetic observatories in polar regions, such as now exist at Sodankyla, Lerwick, Meanook, Godhavn, Tromsø, and Fairbanks (Alaska). Knowledge of the magnetic conditions in polar regions was therefore based on the observations of scientific expeditions, lasting in few cases for more than a year. Many such expeditions, both to the Arctic and Antarctic

* The curve 1(a) in Fig. 10, p. 43, is the only exception. This is referred to later (p. 96).

regions, have included magnetic work in their programme. In the years 1882-3 and 1932-3, called the International Polar Years, many of the leading nations co-operated in extensive schemes of observation in the polar regions, sending expeditions to various stations there, which operated magnetic (and meteorological) recording instruments for about a year : these furnish the larger part of our information on magnetic disturbance in high latitudes.

The form of the D field in the polar regions is found to be closely linked with the auroral zones. The lines of equal frequency of auroral occurrence (called *isochasms*) were delineated by Fritz from the study of long series of auroral observations ; the northern auroral zone, that is, the isochasm of maximum frequency, is an oval curve of about 23° angular radius, centred approximately at the north pole of the earth's magnetic axis. Auroral observations in the Antarctic are insufficient to enable the southern isochasms to be drawn, but they are probably similar to the northern ones, being disposed round and within a principal isochasm forming the southern auroral zone, and centred at the southern pole of the magnetic axis.

The most striking change in the character of the D field as the auroral zone is approached from lower latitudes can be distinguished already at the latitude of Sitka, as illustrated in Figs. 9-11 or 21-23. It is the growing predominance of the S_D part of the field (the part depending on local time, and therefore corresponding to a field appearing stationary as viewed from the sun) in comparison with the part that is symmetrical about the earth's axis—the storm-time field. In the tropics the range of the storm-time variations exceeds that of S_D ; this can be seen from the left-hand curve in Fig. 20, compared with the curves $5(b)$ in Figs. 21-23 : or again from the " all-day minus quiet-day " H.F. difference for Honolulu in the Table on p. 86 (viz. 10γ), as compared with the range of the curves $5(c)$ in Figs. 9-11. But at Sitka the " all-day minus quiet-day " H.F. difference is only 3γ, while the range of the corresponding S_D curves, $1(c)$ in Figs. 9-11, is larger (and in the V.F., much larger).

The storm-time variation in the polar regions, corresponding to that shown for lower latitudes in Fig. 20, has not been determined, because until recently there has not been material for polar observatories extending over a sufficient number of years to include many magnetic storms. But the method already used to examine the similarity of very weak to strong disturbance, as regards the storm-time field, can be applied to the polar regions, since it involves merely the determination of the all-day minus quiet-day means. In order that the results thus obtained may be fairly comparable with those already given for stations in lower latitudes, the quiet days chosen must number about the same proportion of all days as before, that is, about five per month ; few if any of them may appear quiet as judged by tropical standards, and in fact it seems likely that the variations shown on these days are really almost wholly disturbance variations, the part due to S_q being insignificant in these regions. But the difference between these days and the average of all days will of course correspond to the same relative difference in the disturbance, whether for polar or non-polar latitudes.

The results of such a comparison, made some years ago, are given in Fig. 25. It should before long be possible to include more data in such a figure, derived from the second International Polar Year, but the figure as it stands probably shows the salient facts.

The difference between the all-day and quiet-day means for each station is of course a vector having three components. In polar regions the horizontal component of this vector does not in general lie so nearly along the direction of the whole horizontal force as it does in lower latitudes, and the geographical direction of the horizontal force varies considerably over the region. It is therefore desirable to indicate graphically the direction of the horizontal disturbance vector, as in the figure. This shows ten such vectors, represented by lines drawn from points corresponding to the situation of ten polar observatories. The circles of latitudes 55°, 60°, 70°, 80°, are also shown, and, by a dotted line, the auroral zone as drawn by Fritz,

It appears that, on the whole, these horizontal disturbance vectors diverge from a point or small region near the centre of the auroral zone, or the pole of the earth's magnetic axes ; they are decidedly not symmetrical about the geographical pole.

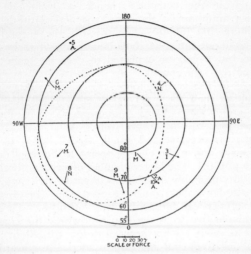

FIG. 25.—All-day minus quiet-day mean horizontal force vectors in high latitudes. 1. Cap Thordsen. 2. Bossekop. 3. Nova Zembla. 4. Ssagastyr. 5. Sitka. 6. Fort Rae. 7. Kingua Fjord. 8. Godthaab. 9. Jan Mayen. 10. Sodankyla.

M = Morning V.F. maximum.
A = Afternoon V.F. maximum.
I = V.F. irregular.
N = V.F., no record, or unreliable.

The average change in the mean horizontal force thus consists approximately of a reduction in the component of the force along the meridians through the magnetic axis. In this respect it resembles the corresponding change of horizontal force in lower latitudes ; but in the polar regions the reduction is larger, varying up to 20γ, whereas in lower latitudes the maximum, which occurs at the equator, is about 10γ (these figures are probably substantially comparable, though not exactly so, because they are derived from material for different years and days).

The average storm-time change of force in the horizontal plane is thus everywhere a decrease, which has a maximum at the equator, whence its value decreases towards a minimum at about 60° magnetic latitude, afterwards increasing rapidly again towards the auroral zone. The data do not suffice to show clearly how it varies within the zone, but it may be expected to decrease again to zero at the centre of the zone.

As regards the vertical force, the all-day mean appears to be higher than the quiet-day mean at Fort Rae, Nova Zembla and Kingua Fjord (stations 6, 3, 7 in Fig. 25), by about 18γ, 19γ, 6γ respectively. At stations 2, 10, 5 the change is negative and small, viz., − 4, − 4, − 3γ. At stations 1 and 9 the change seems to be small and its sign is doubtful. The larger changes of vertical force, here quoted, are probably reliable as regards sign and order of magnitude ; they much exceed the corresponding changes of vertical force in lower latitudes. These are small and positive from the equator (where the change is zero) up to about 55° northern latitude ; then they change sign (to negative) and increase numerically towards the auroral zone. A further change of sign, to positive values, occurs at or within this zone, where the large differences above quoted are found (the stations 6 and 3, shown outside the zone, in this respect behave like station 7, which is certainly within the zone).

Further within the zone it seems likely that the vertical-force difference will decrease again towards the axis of magnetization, but data on this point are wanting.

In the Antarctic the data for Cape Evans (77·6° S, 166·4° E) show that the " all-day minus quiet-day " mean difference in the (upward) vertical force is an increase of 5γ ; this result is confirmed by the (naturally larger) difference of 12γ, with the same sign, between the mean of the five most disturbed days per month, and all days. Thus at Cape Evans, within the southern auroral zone, disturbance increases the numerical magnitude of the vertical force, as in the arctic region.

S_D IN HIGH LATITUDES

These " all-day minus quiet-day " differences, though of great interest and importance, since they represent the average of the storm-time variations, are of smaller magnitude than the local-time, or S_D, part of the disturbance field, in polar regions. This will next be considered.

Fig. 23 (curves (b), (c)) shows that S_D in the vertical force maintains a constant phase from the equator to as far north as Sitka, with a morning minimum and an evening maximum ; the amplitude increases greatly with latitude. The increase persists beyond the (magnetic) latitude of Sitka—where the range, for all-days minus quiet-days, is about 20γ (cf. Fig. 10, curve 1(c)) to Bossekop, where the range exceeds 100γ. The curves for Bossekop and other polar stations are illustrated in Fig. 26. These curves, with the exception of the one for Nova Zembla, are of similar

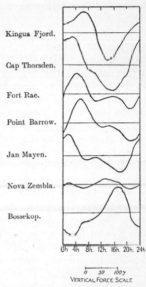

FIG. 26.—Annual mean daily variation of vertical force in Polar regions.

very large range, but the most remarkable feature is that their phases are all opposite to that for Bossekop and the other stations of lower latitude ; the curve for Nova Zembla is transitional between the two sets of curves. The reversal of phase seems to occur within a narrow belt of magnetic latitude adjacent to the auroral zone.

This reversal of phase of the vertical force (S_D) daily variation, in a region where on the two sides of the dividing line the range is itself so large, constitutes what is perhaps the most striking of all the average characteristics of the field of world-wide magnetic disturbance.

The " all-day minus quiet-day " S_D variation in the horizontal plane is likewise large in polar regions, the range being of the order 50γ. This greatly exceeds the range in lower latitudes, and even that at Sitka, in magnetic latitude 60°.

In passing northwards from Sitka and crossing to within the auroral zone the S_D variation in the horizontal plane experiences a striking change of type, which is not simply a reversal as in the case of the vertical force. The change is best shown by the horizontal-force vector diagrams for S_D. At Sitka the diagram still bears some resemblance to the roughly oval form, elongated in the direction transverse to the magnetic meridian, shown at Greenwich and other stations in similar latitudes. But for stations quite near the auroral zone, like Ssagastyr, Sodankyla, Nova Zembla and Bossekop, in magnetic latitudes 61°, 64°, 65°, 67°, the diagram is very narrow in this direction (that is, in the direction parallel to the auroral zone), and much elongated in the direction normal to the zone : cf. Fig. 27. The maximum poleward force occurs at from 15^h to 18^h, and the opposite minimum at about 0^h. On passing well inside the zone the vector diagram again becomes oval, indeed nearly circular. This is shown by the diagrams for Kingua Fjord and Cape Evans, in magnetic latitudes 78° N. and 79° S. (note that these two curves are described in opposite senses). The curves for other stations are of similar or intermediate type.

Fig. 27 shows the horizontal force S_D vector diagram, derived from all-days minus quiet-days for Sitka, Sodankyla, Bossekop, Kingua Fjord and Cape Evans. In each case the magnitude and direction of the horizontal-force disturbance vector shown in Fig. 25 is indicated by a line drawn from the origin. This enables the orientation of the diagram, and therefore of the S_D disturbance vector at any local time, relative to the auroral zone, to be inferred by comparison with Fig. 25. It also shows, for the stations within or very near the zone, how greatly S_D exceeds the average of the storm-time variation, represented by this vector from the origin. It should be care-

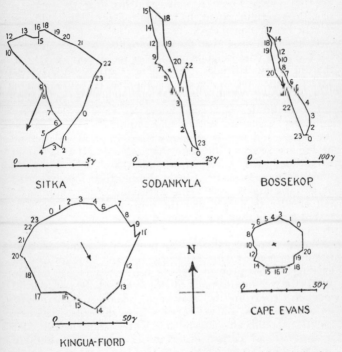

FIG. 27.—Horizontal-force vector diagrams in high latitudes (N. or S.) (p. 94).

fully noted that the separate diagrams in Fig. 27 are drawn to different scales, to render them of similar size and so to facilitate comparison between their different forms.

The average characteristics of disturbance in polar regions, so far considered, are those associated with the degree of disturbance existing on average days as compared with quiet days. But the facts described in pages 83-88 suggest that the distribution and development of the disturbance field may remain fairly constant, and independent of the intensity of the disturbance, in middle and low latitudes. There is some evidence that the same is true, to a certain extent, in high latitudes. This evidence will be briefly considered.

It has been seen that the S_D variation in polar regions is very great (the range being 50γ or more) compared with that in lower latitudes. Even on relatively quiet days, such as the five quietest per month, there remains a certain amount of disturbance, including S_D. In middle and low latitudes S_D is small compared with S_q, the normal quiet-day variation, but in high latitudes it may exceed the latter, and wholly or partly mask it. Curves $1(a)$, (c) of Fig. 10 seem to illustrate this: Curve $1(c)$ is of larger amplitude than curve $1(a)$, and the latter, which is intended to represent S_q alone, appears to be compounded of two variations, one being a residue of S_D, similar to but smaller than $1(c)$, and the other the true S_q, similar to but smaller than the S_q shown by the curves 3, 4, 5, (a) in Fig. 11.

Within the auroral zone S_q probably becomes insignificant compared with even the average amount of S_D existing in the mean of the five quietest days per month. If so, the vector diagrams for the whole daily variation of magnetic force in the horizontal plane, on quiet days, on average days, and on the five most disturbed days per month, should all be similar. Chree showed that this is the case for certain observatories within the southern auroral zone, a fact which seems to be a partial confirmation of the view that the general character of the disturbance field, in polar as well as in lower latitudes, does not vary greatly while the intensity alters considerably.

At polar stations quite near the auroral zone, however, there may be considerable change in the type of S_D, and in the " all-days minus quiet-days " mean difference in vertical force, as the intensity of disturbance increases.

This is because of the complicated structure of the average disturbance field in the polar regions, and its close connection with the auroral zone. This zone seems to extend and move to a lower latitude during periods of intense disturbance, so that a station which is normally near but outside the zone may during a magnetic storm be under or within it. If so, the disturbance changes at the station during slight disturbance may be radically different from those which occur there during a storm, even though, in relation to the zone, the character of the disturbance field may be similar in the two cases.

The Irregular Disturbance Fluctuations D_i

Besides the regular storm-time part and the regular diurnal part of the disturbance field, there are the *irregular* disturbance fluctuations D_i. They are averaged out in the processes by which the first two parts of the field are determined.

D_i shows unlimited variety in detail, but on the average it has a notable dependence on latitude and on local time ; that is to say, it has on the average a well-marked geographical distribution of intensity, which so far as longitude is concerned depends on longitude relative to the sun, and not on absolute longitude. Hence, like the S_q field and the S_D field, its average distribution over the earth is definite (at any particular season) as viewed from the sun.

In the following brief account D_i will be used to denote the average intensity of D_i over a considerable space of time, either a number of whole days or, when considering the daily variation of D_i, over a number of days for a particular hour. This usage will obviate the need for the continual repetition of the word " average." It must be understood that on particular occasions the distribution of D_i may depart from this average distribution.

As regards distribution in latitude, D_i is least in low latitudes, and increases with the latitude ; the increase is slow until near the auroral zone, where it becomes very

7

rapid; there is a pronounced maximum of intensity of D_i under or nearly under the zone. Further within the zone the intensity decreases again, in summer to about half the maximum, and in winter to about a fifth. Even this winter value of the polar minimum of D_i is several times as large as the intensity of D_i at the equator.

The distribution of D_i in longitude relative to the meridian containing the sun, i.e. its variation with local time, likewise shows a marked relationship with the auroral zone. In the latitudes between the two auroral zones, that is, up to at least $65°$ magnetic latitude, D_i has a simple daily variation, with its maximum in the evening; as the auroral zone is approached the hour of maximum gets later, from about 21^h at $55°$ to midnight at $70°$. Up to this latitude the form of the daily variation of D_i does not vary much either with season or with the general intensity of magnetic disturbance.

Between $70°$ and $80°$ magnetic latitude—within the auroral zone—the curve of daily variation of D_i changes its character, in a way that depends greatly on the season and on the general intensity of the D field. Above $80°$ latitude, that is, in the central region well within the auroral zone, D_i again shows one dominant maximum, but this is now invariably in the forenoon, between about 8^h and 11^h; in the winter there is in addition a secondary late evening maximum. In the zone $70°$-$80°$ the transition is made from the evening to the dominant morning maximum.

THE ELECTRIC CURRENT-SYSTEMS ASSOCIATED WITH THE D FIELD

Harmonic analysis of the D field shows that its origin, like that of S_q, is partly external and partly internal. The internal part (D^i) can reasonably be explained as due to electric currents induced within the earth by the external part of the D field (D^e). Since the storm-time part of the D field varies more slowly with the time than the other parts (S_D and D_i), its induced currents penetrate further down into the conducting core of the earth (p. 54) than the S_q or S_D currents. They appear to show that the electric conductivity of the core increases downwards rather rapidly, in the region below 160 miles' depth.

The origin of the D^e field is unknown, and opinions differ even as to the location of its source. There is good evidence that the field near the auroral zone is due to strong currents flowing along the zone at a height of at least 100 km. above the ground, the direction being eastward at certain local times and westward at others ; their intensity seems to be of the order of a million amperes. These currents flow in our atmosphere. Since their direction is not the same all round the zone, they must complete their paths outside the zone ; this raises the important question, whether they flow wholly within the atmosphere, or whether they enter the atmosphere from outside (and, of course, afterwards leave the atmosphere, since the earth cannot continually accumulate electric charge). Up to the present the magnetic data have not yielded a decisive answer to this question.

It seems possible that the D^e field in non-polar latitudes is, at least in part, caused by electric currents outside the atmosphere. On the other hand, hypotheses as to electric currents outside the atmosphere are quite speculative. It has often been suggested, however, that the storm-time part of the D^e field, in non-polar latitudes, is due to a great ring current round the earth, the current being westward during the main phase. The suggested values for the radius of this ring current have ranged widely—from a few earth-radii, to values exceeding the radius of the moon's orbit.

While the position and size of the current-systems responsible for the D^e field are so much in doubt, the theory of the origin of these currents must remain even more speculative than in the case of S_q. The subject is considered further at the end of the next chapter.

CHAPTER VI

SOLAR RELATIONS WITH MAGNETIC DISTURBANCE

IN this chapter the variation of the general intensity of the D field, from day to day and from year to year, will be considered. Studies of these variations may be based on the records of one element at a single observatory, or on some index of disturbance, like the international daily magnetic character figure, depending on data from many observatories. These character figures, however, may not be well suited for the study of variations over a long period of time, since their " scale-value " is not definite.

THE RELATION OF MAGNETIC DISTURBANCE TO THE SUNSPOT CYCLE *

One outstanding relation which is thoroughly established is that disturbance is more frequent, and on the average more intense, near the epoch of maximum sunspots than near the minimum sunspot epoch. Hence the intensity of D undergoes a cycle with a period of approximately eleven years, like the sunspots.

This is illustrated by Fig. 28, which shows the frequency of (lunar) days of different range in Greenwich magnetic declination (after abstracting the S_q part of the variation, which itself waxes and wanes with the annual mean sunspottedness) for different groups of years : the curves are marked α, β, γ, δ, ϵ, in descending order of mean annual sunspot number from maximum to minimum. The figure shows that in years of sunspot maximum (α) both the mean range and the proportion of high ranges are much greater than in years of sunspot minimum (ϵ).

* See p. 29.

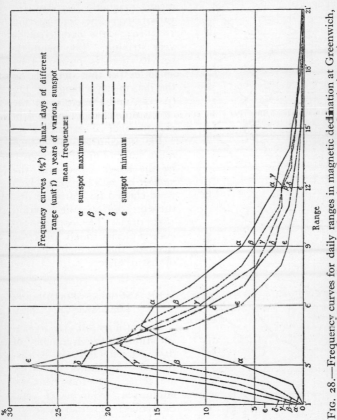

Frequency curves (%) of lunar days of different range (unit 1') in years of various sunspot mean frequencies

α sunspot maximum
β
γ
δ
ε sunspot minimum

FIG. 28.—Frequency curves for daily ranges in magnetic declination at Greenwich, for years of different solar spottedness ($\alpha > \beta > \gamma > \delta > \epsilon$), (p. 100).

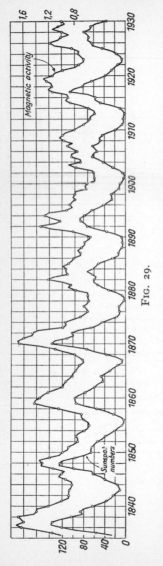

FIG. 29.

Fig. 29 shows how the annual mean sunspot numbers (lower curve) and the annual mean magnetic activity (u) varied over the long period 1835-1930; the parallelism is very striking. The magnetic activity here is measured by an index (u) that depends on the day-to-day change of D_m (p. 35), and therefore on the storm-time changes in the field at a number of stations.

Fig. 30 contrasts the annual mean sunspot numbers (shown by the lower curve) with the *number* of days per year which were classed (at Paris) as disturbed, during the period 1882-1923. The correspondence is clearly much less close than for the average *intensity* of disturbance.

THE ANNUAL VARIATION OF DISTURBANCE

Fig. 31 illustrates the *annual* variation in the frequency of days classed (at Paris) as disturbed. It shows that they are more numerous near the equinoxes (March 21 and September 21) than near the solstices. Fig. 32 illustrates the annual variation of the magnetic activity, measured by u as in Fig. 29; the upper, middle and lower curves refer to disturbed

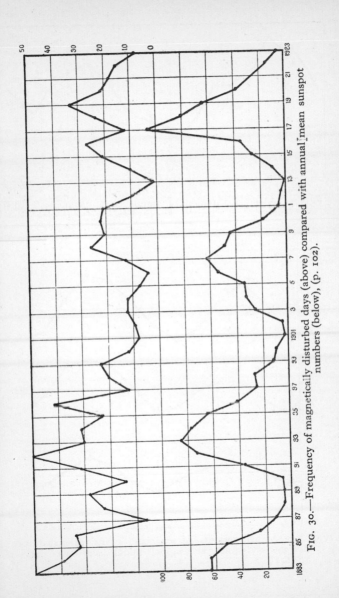

FIG. 30.—Frequency of magnetically disturbed days (above) compared with annual mean sunspot numbers (below), (p. 102).

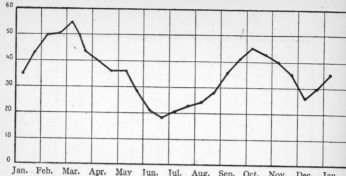

Jan. Feb. Mar. Apr. May Jun. Jul. Aug. Sep. Oct. Nov. Dec. Jan.

FIG. 31.—Annual variation of frequency of magnetically disturbed days (p. 102).

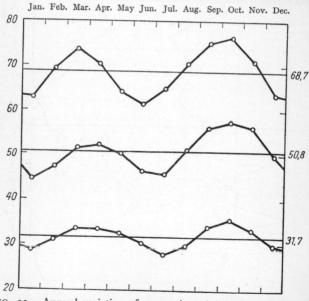

Jan. Feb. Mar. Apr. May Jun. Jul. Aug. Sep. Oct. Nov. Dec.

FIG. 32.—Annual variation of magnetic activity (u) in disturbed, average, and quiet years (upper, middle, and lower curves), (p. 102).

years, average years, and quiet years respectively. Figs.
31, 32 show that both the frequency and the intensity of
disturbance vary in a similar way throughout the year. The
cause of this variation is not yet understood.

The Solar Rotation Period

The sun rotates about its axis, as is shown by the motion
of sunspots across the disc (and in other ways). It does not
rotate as a rigid body; the rotation is most rapid at the
equator, and decreases steadily towards the poles. But
the mean period of rotation (relative to the earth, which itself
has an orbital motion round the sun), for the latitudes in
which sunspots occur, is approximately 27·3 days.

Since many sunspots last for more than one solar rotation
period, the same spot may contribute to the daily sunspot
numbers not only for the days of its first appearance on the
disc, but for later days after the sun has carried it round into
view again. If the spots were permanent, there would be
a definite 27-day periodicity in the daily sunspot numbers;
but since spots are born, and disappear, at irregular intervals, all that the daily sunspot numbers show, on account
of the rotation, is a *tendency* for recurrence of the same sunspot number after twenty-seven days. This is well illustrated in Fig. 33*b*, where the magnitude of the daily sunspot
numbers is represented for each of a long series of days
(1928-1931), by the degree of blackness of small squares,
one for each day. The days are arranged in rows of twenty-
seven, so that each row represents one rotation period. It
is evident that dark squares in different rows tend to recur
near the same column; this means that days of relatively
high sunspot number tend to recur after a lapse of twenty-
seven days, or a solar rotation; the same applies to spotless
days. The diagram shows that particular regions on the
sun (represented by different vertical columns of the
diagram) tend to remain quiet or disturbed over long
periods, periods much longer than the life of individual
spots. Sometimes a disturbed region lapses into quietness

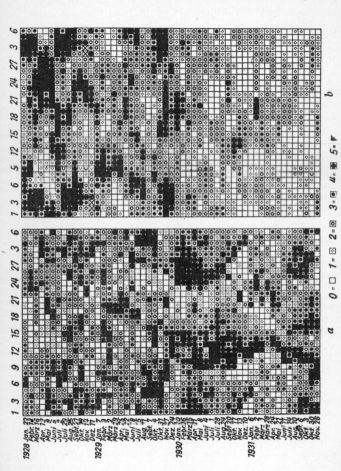

FIG. 33.—27-day time-patterns, for successive groups (rows) of 27 days, of daily magnetic activity (a) and daily sunspottedness (b), (p. 105, 107).

0 = □   1 = ▨   2 = ⊡   3 = ◉   4 = ▨   5 = ▼

for a time, and afterwards becomes disturbed again. The decline from the sunspot maximum in 1928 is also well shown.

The Daily Sunspottedness and the Daily Magnetic Activity

The daily magnetic character figures can be represented in a manner similar to that used in Fig. 33*b* for the daily sunspot numbers. This is done in Fig. 33*a* for the same period as that to which Fig. 33*a* refers. The blackest squares represent the days magnetically most disturbed, and the blank squares the quietest days. The days are arranged in the same 27-day rows in both figures. If the earth's magnetic activity were closely dependent on (or highly correlated with) the presence and extent of spots on the sun, as Fig. 30 might suggest, the "patterns" of the two Figs. 33*a*, *b* should be very similar. It is evident that this is not so. Quiet magnetic periods sometimes coincide with much spottedness on the sun, and conversely magnetic disturbance may occur when the sun's disc is free from spots. It would therefore seem that sunspots themselves are not responsible for disturbing the earth's magnetic field, but that the cause, on the sun, of magnetic disturbance on the earth, waxes and wanes in frequency and intensity throughout the sunspot cycle, in *general* but not *detailed* correspondence with the sunspots.

The 27-Day Recurrence Tendency in Magnetic Activity

Fig. 33*a* shows another important property of magnetic disturbance. Though its pattern does not agree with that of Fig. 33*b*, it shares one characteristic with it. Black squares in successive rows tend to be grouped near the same column, and similarly for light squares. This means that magnetic disturbance tends to recur in (about) 27 days, that is, after a solar rotation. As in the case of the sunspot numbers, this tendency does not constitute a permanent periodicity, for the recurrences are from time to time interrupted, or cease altogether. The recurrence tendency shown by magnetic disturbance is another indication, independent of that afforded by Fig. 30, that magnetic disturbance is due to some solar cause. It indicates that there are regions on the sun effective in causing magnetic disturbance : that these regions rotate with the sun : and that they may remain effective for more than one solar rotation period—often throughout many such periods. Solar physicists have not yet succeeded in detecting any visible solar characteristic associated with these regions ; if they should in the future do so, the discovery should be of great value in enabling magnetic disturbance to be foretold by observation of the sun. Bartels has called these " magnetically effective " regions M regions. There is, of course, no suggestion that they exert a magnetic influence by their own magnetic field : powerful local magnetic fields, associated with sunspots, are indeed observed on the sun (by means of the Zeeman effect), but their intensity sinks to insignificance at a distance far less than that which separates the earth from the sun.

CHREE'S RECURRENCE DIAGRAMS

The recurrence tendency of magnetic disturbance can also be illustrated in the following way. The days of character figure 2 during a certain period are picked out. The character figures for each of these days, and for a few days before and a number of days afterwards—maybe 30, maybe 60 or even more—are written out in rows, one for each of the selected disturbed days. Means of each column of figures are then formed, giving the mean character figure for the days preceding or following the selected days by a certain interval. The column for the selected days has, of course, the mean 2 ; the means for the other days are less than 2. Fig. 34 shows a graph of means so formed : the important feature is that 27 or 28 days after the maximum corresponding to the selected days, there is another maximum, showing a tendency for disturbance to recur after such an interval. Similar graphs may be constructed from series of days following on selected quiet days (character figure o) ; the graph shows a deep minimum for the selected days, and a smaller minimum 27 or 28 days later.

Fig. 34 is based on series of 35 days following (and 5 preceding) the disturbed days : graphs have been drawn from much longer series of days, and show recurring peaks

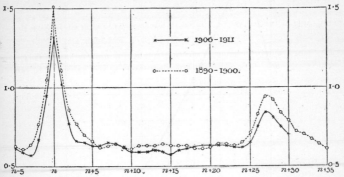

Fig. 34.—Average daily magnetic character figures for days preceding and following a set of selected magnetically disturbed days (*n*).

of diminishing magnitude after two, three or even more intervals of 27 or 28 days. Such diagrams constitute perhaps the most convincing proof of the existence of the recurrence tendency.

INDIVIDUAL SUNSPOTS AND MAGNETIC STORMS

Though magnetic disturbance may occur on days when the sun has no spots, it is found that in general the greatest disturbances coincide with the presence of great spots near the centre of the sun. Great spots are, however, by no means always associated with notable magnetic disturbance. These and the other facts already described suggest that terrestrial magnetic disturbance is due to some emission from limited areas on the sun, often but not always associated with sunspots : and that this emission is corpuscular, being confined to a limited "beam" or stream, issuing in general in a roughly radial direction from the sun. The beam will lag behind the sun in its rotation, but its form will rotate with the sun (just as a

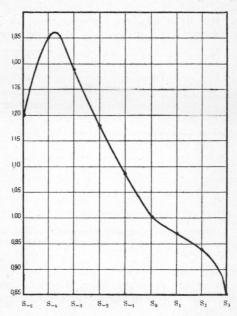

FIG. 35.—Average daily sunspot numbers for days preceding and following a set of selected magnetically disturbed days (S_0).

stream of water issuing from a rotating hose will seem to rotate after the hose—though not, of course, like a rigid body). If the stream encounters the earth, it produces a magnetic disturbance : but many streams may miss the earth, thus corresponding to spots unaccompanied by disturbance.

The Time of Travel from the Sun

If the above ideas are correct, and the emission of the solar agent responsible for magnetic disturbance is roughly radial, then the time of travel of this agent from the sun to the earth can be determined : because the matter which is to affect the earth must be emitted when the area of emission is in the centre of the sun's disc, or at least on the central meridian of the sun ; * whereas when the matter reaches the earth, the area will have moved on in the direction of the sun's rotation. Assuming that the emitting area is associated with a visible spot, the time of travel to the earth is measured by the time taken for the spot (identified conjecturally with the disturbance) to travel from the central meridian to the meridian on which it lies at the time of the disturbance. This interval is found to be between 1 and 4 days.

The same idea can be applied in another way. Selecting a number of days of magnetic disturbance, the daily sunspot numbers for these and neighbouring days are tabulated, in rows, one for each selected day. Means in each column are taken, and their ratios to the mean for the selected days are plotted on a graph ; Fig. 35 shows the curve thus obtained by Maurain, from 121 disturbed days selected at Paris from a period of 10 years of feeble solar activity. It shows a weak maximum of the daily sunspot numbers, occurring on the average $2\frac{1}{2}$ days before the occurrence of the selected disturbances.

Thus the available evidence suggests that the time of travel of the solar agent is from 1 to 4 days, corresponding to a mean speed of from 1100 to 270 miles per second. Since this is far less than the speed of light, it is additional evidence for the corpuscular character of the solar agent.

---

* This statement must be modified slightly if the slow orbital revolution of the earth round the sun is taken into account.

The Deflecting Influence of the Earth's Magnetic Field

The special geographical distribution of magnetic disturbance, and its association with the polar lights or auroræ, give perhaps the most convincing indication of the corpuscular character of the solar agent responsible for these two terrestrial phenomena. For the polar incidence of auroræ and of the intense disturbance field near the auroral zone receives a simple and natural explanation through the hypothesis that these phenomena are due to electrically charged corpuscles entering the atmosphere from outside, which are guided towards the polar regions by the earth's magnetic field.

It seems necessary that the corpuscles shall travel from the sun in streams containing nearly equal numbers of particles of opposite charges ; otherwise the excess charge of one sign would be dispersed by mutual electrostatic repulsion.

Much still remains obscure concerning the way in which such streams of corpuscles will act near the earth and after entering the earth's atmosphere.

INDEX

PRINTED IN GREAT BRITAIN AT THE UNIVERSITY PRESS, ABERDEEN